42

P950

DUPLICATE

DUPLICATE

Superfluid Physics

INTERNATIONAL SERIES IN PURE AND APPLIED PHYSICS

LEONARD I. SCHIFF, *Consulting Editor*

Allis and Herlin   Thermodynamics and Statistical Mechanics
Becker   Introduction to Theoretical Mechanics
Clark   Applied X-Rays
Collin   Field Theory of Guided Waves
Evans   The Atomic Nucleus
Finkelnburg   Atomic Physics
Ginzton   Microwave Measurements
Green   Nuclear Physics
Gurney   Introduction to Statistical Mechanics
Hall   Introduction to Electron Microscopy
Hardy and Perrin   The Principles of Optics
Harnwell   Electricity and Electromagnetism
Harnwell and Livingood   Experimental Atomic Physics
Harnwell and Stephens   Atomic Physics
Henley and Thirring   Elementary Quantum Field Theory
Houston   Principles of Mathematical Physics
Hund   High-frequency Measurements
Kennard   Kinetic Theory of Gases
Lane   Superfluid Physics
Leighton   Principles of Modern Physics
Lindsay   Mechanical Radiation
Livingston and Blewett   Particle Accelerators
Middleton   An Introduction to Statistical Communication Theory
Morse   Vibration and Sound
Morse and Feshbach   Methods of Theoretical Physics
Muskat   Physical Principles of Oil Production
Present   Kinetic Theory of Gases
Read   Dislocations in Crystals
Richtmyer, Kennard, and Lauritsen   Introduction to Modern Physics
Schiff   Quantum Mechanics
Seitz   The Modern Theory of Solids
Slater   Introduction to Chemical Physics
Slater   Quantum Theory of Atomic Structure, Vol. I
Slater   Quantum Theory of Atomic Structure, Vol. II
Slater   Quantum Theory of Matter
Slater and Frank   Electromagnetism
Slater and Frank   Introduction to Theoretical Physics
Slater and Frank   Mechanics
Smythe   Static and Dynamic Electricity
Stratton   Electromagnetic Theory
Thorndike   Mesons: A Summary of Experimental Facts
Townes and Schawlow   Microwave Spectroscopy
White   Introduction to Atomic Spectra

The late F. K. Richtmyer was Consulting Editor of the series from its inception in 1929 to his death in 1939.   Lee A. DuBridge was Consulting Editor from 1939 to 1946; and G. P. Harnwell from 1947 to 1954.

SUPERFLUID PHYSICS

CECIL T. LANE

PROFESSOR OF PHYSICS
YALE UNIVERSITY

NNDC

McGRAW-HILL BOOK COMPANY, INC.   1962

New York   San Francisco   Toronto   London

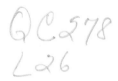

SUPERFLUID PHYSICS

36237

THE MAPLE PRESS COMPANY, YORK, PA

Preface

This book is based on a course of lectures which I have given to first-year graduate students in physics for the past ten years. The aim of the course is twofold: first, to provide a general survey of superfluidity for those students who do not intend to specialize in low-temperature physics; and second, to provide some sort of introduction to the subject for a smaller number of beginning students who wish to take a degree in the experimental side of this specialty.

Accordingly, the treatment throughout is elementary in nature and involves, mathematically, little more than an undergraduate knowledge of calculus. In other words, the main emphasis is upon the physical principles involved, rather than the theoretical subtleties which would have to be included in an exhaustive treatment.

Over the ten-year period the advance of the subject has been very rapid. This required reviewing the content of the course at frequent intervals, adding new material, and eliminating some of the older material when advances in research showed this to be desirable. In the present text I have tried to keep a fair balance between the old and the new, and it is in this selection that the author's personal preferences and opinions intrude most heavily.

I have, of course, profited by reading prior books and review articles. A short bibliography, which is not exhaustive, is included in an appendix, together with an attempt to evaluate these books for the benefit of the nonspecialist.

C. T. Lane

Contents

CHAPTER 1

Production and Handling
of Liquefied Gases

THERMODYNAMICS OF FREE EXPANSION

Liquid helium, liquid air (or nitrogen), and, on occasion, liquid hydrogen are the indispensable tools of the low-temperature physicist. Their production involves nineteenth-century thermodynamics in a form, however, which nowadays is rather more familiar to the chemical engineer than to the average student of physics.

In principle, a gas must be cooled in order to liquefy it, and either or both of two processes are universally employed. The first of these, associated with the names of Joule and Thomson (Lord Kelvin), depends on the empirical fact that if any gas, at suitable temperature and under pressure, is permitted to expand in volume, a cooling of the gas results. This process is, thermodynamically, highly irreversible. The second process allows the compressed gas to expand and do external work in, for instance, an engine or turbine. This process is closely reversible.

Figure 1 is an Andrews diagram (familiar to all students of elementary physics) for carbon dioxide and is typical of all gases. At temperatures well removed from the critical ($\sim$31°C) the gas obeys Boyle's law tolerably well. But below the critical temperature (e.g., $t_3 = 10$°C in Fig. 1) the gas splits into a liquid and vapor phase wherein the pressure is independent of the volume (region ab, Fig. 1) and

1

depends on the temperature alone. The important point is that the CO_2 must be cooled below 31°C in order for any liquid to form at all, no matter what the pressure may be. Hence refrigeration is indispensable to any gas-liquefaction process.

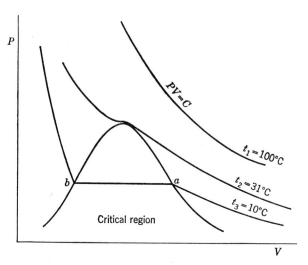

FIG. 1. Andrews diagram for carbon dioxide. The pressure P is plotted against the volume V for three temperatures.

This simple diagram would be of slight value to the designer of a liquefier, since the actual cooling process, the Joule-Thomson effect, does not appear on it. We recall that the Joule-Thomson coefficient is defined as

$$\mu = \left(\frac{\partial T}{\partial p}\right)_h \tag{1}$$

where T and p are the Kelvin temperature and pressure, respectively, and h is the enthalpy. Now it can be shown, quite generally, that

$$\mu = \frac{1}{C_p}\left[T\left(\frac{\partial V}{\partial T}\right)_p - V\right] \tag{2}$$

where V is the volume and C_p the specific heat at constant pressure. For an ideal gas whose "equation of state" is

$$PV = RT$$

expression (2) vanishes, but μ may be either positive or negative for any real gas. If an equation of state for any real gas existed, expression (2) would be of great utility to our designer, but no usable equation exists for any gas.   Hence we must fall back on empirical determination of $\mu = f(p,V,T)$.

Before we consider this, it is necessary to prove a general proposition concerning the enthalpy function.   To do this, we make use of a trick, common in thermodynamics, illustrated in Fig. 2.   Consider unit mass of any gas initially at pressure p_1, volume V_1, and thermal energy (i.e., energy due to the rms velocity of the atoms) U_1.   Let this volume be forced at constant pressure p_1 through a fine opening which offers a resistance to the gas flow so that its pressure falls to p_2, its volume

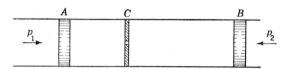

FIG. 2. Arrangement for a free-expansion process.

increases to V_2, and its thermal energy becomes U_2.   We could, in principle, accomplish this by using a pair of frictionless pistons A and B (Fig. 2) with pressures p_1 and p_2 acting as shown.   As the volume AC (V_1) is reduced to zero, piston B sweeps out the volume $V_2 = BC$. Applying conservation of energy, we have

Work done in system $= p_1V_1 - p_2V_2$
Change in energy $= U_2 - U_1$
Hence $\quad p_1V_1 - p_2V_2 = U_2 - U_1$
that is, $\quad U_1 + p_1V_1 = U_2 + p_2V_2$
or $\qquad\qquad h_1 = h_2$ \hfill (3)

In words, the enthalpy remains constant in this process of "free expansion," which is sometimes called a throttling process by engineers. We note that the process must be slow enough so that no kinetic energy is acquired by the expanded gas.

We have described what amounts to a Joule-Thomson expansion, and this suggests that an enthalpy versus temperature diagram would be more useful than Fig. 1.   By way of an introduction, suppose we calculate the enthalpy of an ideal gas:

$$h = U + pV = U + RT = C_vT + RT = C_pT \qquad (4)$$

where C_v is the specific heat at constant volume.   Since C_p is independent of temperature for such a gas, this plots as a straight line on the diagram.   Now it is true that any of the "permanent" gases at vanish-

ingly small pressure (say a few millimeters of mercury) approximate an
ideal gas very well. But for real gases at elevated pressures the
enthalpy turns out to be a function of pressure as well as temperature.
Figure 3 shows the essentials of such a diagram for nitrogen, wherein
the dotted curve marks the boundary of the liquid-vapor region; a few
temperatures are shown for reference, as well as three isobars, i.e.,

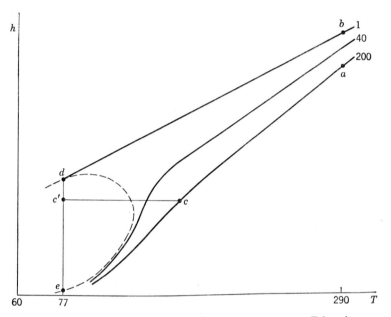

FIG. 3. Schematic diagram of enthalpy h versus temperature T for nitrogen.

1, 40, and 200 atm, respectively. Clearly, a Joule-Thomson expansion
would be represented on the diagram by a horizontal line ($dh = 0$) connecting any two pressure curves. Also,

$$dh = dU + p\,dV + V\,dp$$
$$= dq + V\,dp$$

Hence
$$\left(\frac{\partial h}{\partial T}\right)_p = \left(\frac{\partial q}{\partial T}\right)_p = C_p \tag{5}$$

Thus the slopes of the lines give the specific heat at constant pressure.
We wish to emphasize again, however, that these diagrams are strictly
empirical, being evolved from actual measurements of $p = f(V,T)$,
specific heats, latent heats, etc.

In order to illustrate the utility of these data, consider the simplest possible device which could be used to liquefy, say, air (Fig. 4). This consists of a "heat exchanger," a needle valve, and a container to receive the condensed air; the whole is thermally insulated from contact with the surroundings. We have chosen the very simplest heat exchanger extant, namely, a pipe within a pipe. No means for removing the liquid is shown, but this is irrelevant to the present discussion.

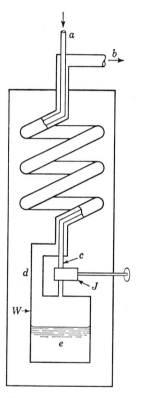

FIG. 4. Diagram of a simple gas liquefier.

High-pressure air (~200 atm) at room temperature (~290°K) is admitted to the inner pipe at a. Upon reaching the valve J, its pressure is reduced to about 1 atm and it enters vessel W, whence it returns through the space between the two pipes and is exhausted to the atmosphere at b. If left to itself for some minutes, liquid air will begin to accumulate in W.

The heart of the process is the Joule-Thomson expansion at the valve plus the action of the heat exchanger. As the enthalpy diagram shows, a Joule-Thomson expansion between any two pressures at any temperature leads to a reduction in temperature of the gas, i.e., a cooling. Thus the air leaving the valve is always colder than that entering it. In its passage back through the exchanger, since the low- and high-pressure streams are in thermal though not in physical contact, heat is continually removed from the high-pressure stream and hence its temperature falls continuously. After a few minutes, the temperature at point c reaches a low steady value. Along the heat exchanger (typically some 20 ft) the difference in temperature between the two streams, at any point measured from a, varies approximately exponentially along the length. Thus $(\Delta T)_{ab} \cong 1°K$ or less, whereas $(\Delta T)_{cd} \cong 30°K$ or more.

When this steady state has been reached, we find that liquid accumulates at a steady rate in W; in other words if, say, unit mass per second enters a, a fraction ε remains as liquid, and accordingly $1 - \varepsilon$ units of mass per second are exhausted at b. The pressure, temperature, and

curve" for the Joule-Thomson effect. Off the curve, on either side, a throttling process will produce either a heating or a cooling. It is most important to understand clearly that the condition $\mu = 0$ for maximum yield refers to the temperature condition at the input to the heat exchanger. The Joule-Thomson valve, where the desired

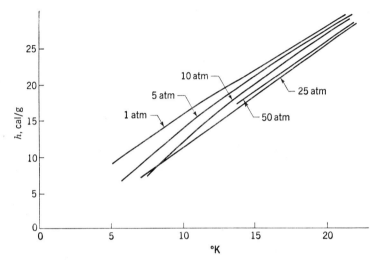

FIG. 6. A part of the enthalpy-temperature diagram for helium.

cooling takes place, is always at a lower temperature, and the cooling effect at this valve is over a wide pressure range. In other words, the cooling is due to the "integral Joule-Thomson effect," i.e.,

$$\Delta T = \int_{p_1}^{p_2} \mu(p,T) \, dp \qquad (9)$$

and is represented by the horizontal line cc' in Fig. 3. The above, of course, is borne out in practice.

A rather more illuminating demonstration of the above is provided by Fig. 6, which shows a portion of the enthalpy-temperature curve for helium. Recalling expression (6) for the yield, we observe that if the input temperature to the heat exchanger were, say, 15°K (which is about that used in practice), then the yield would be greater for an input pressure of 25 atm than would be the case if we used 50 atm. Actually (Fig. 5) at this temperature the maximum yield would be at about 32 atm.

REFRIGERATION WITH EXTERNAL WORK

In the system we have been discussing, all the refrigeration was produced by the Joule-Thomson effect. There is a second method which, in principle, is quite different and which has also been successfully employed to liquefy helium and other gases. To study this, we need still another diagram, also empirically devised, wherein entropy is plotted against temperature. To introduce the diagram, consider once again the case of an ideal gas. For a reversible process the entropy S is defined via the relation

$$dS = \frac{dq}{T} = \frac{C_p \, dT}{T}$$

if the process is carried out at constant pressure. Thus, since C_p is independent of temperature,

$$S = C_p \ln T + \text{const} \tag{10}$$

Hence on the T-S diagram an isobar for an ideal gas would plot as an exponential. It is a fact that, for low enough pressures, the isobars for real gases are indeed of this form. Figure 7 shows the plot for a typical real gas, where it will be seen that an expansion at constant entropy (1 to 3) produces a much larger drop in temperature than the corresponding one at constant enthalpy (1 to 2). The best possibility for achieving the first process is to allow the gas to expand against a retarding force and thus do external work as happens, for instance, in a steam engine or a turbine. The process must be adiabatic and as nearly reversible as possible. For cooling purposes the cycle is very similar to that used in a reciprocating steam engine. A certain mass of gas is admitted at constant pressure p_1, and the piston advances a distance S_0. The supply of gas is then cut off and the gas present in the cylinder allowed to expand to a lower pressure p_2; the piston advances a further distance $(S - S_0)$, where S is the "stroke" of the engine. It is this second process which removes energy from the gas and hence cools it. On the return stroke the piston pushes (without compression) the cold gas from the cylinder into the heat-exchanger system, and the cycle repeats.

We recall that a throttle expansion of an ideal gas produces no cooling; this is not the case for an engine. Using the ideal-gas laws, we may readily show[1] that the amount of heat extracted by a single adiabatic expansion is proportional to

$$S_0 \left[1 - \left(\frac{S_0}{S} \right)^{\gamma-1} \right] \tag{11}$$

where γ is the ratio of the specific heats and S_0 and S are defined above.

Actually, the use of an engine for gas liquefaction was introduced, near the turn of the century, by the French engineer G. Claude, who used it in liquid-air production. The principal technical difficulty

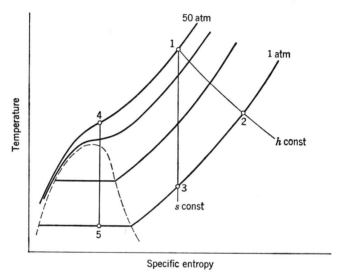

FIG. 7. Schematic of a temperature-entropy diagram for a gas such as helium.

concerns lubrication at these low temperatures—ordinary lubricants freeze solid. At liquid-air temperatures very light oils (such as gasoline) retain some lubricating properties, but at hydrogen or helium temperatures no substance known possesses any lubricating properties at all. This undoubtedly delayed the application of engines to the problem of liquid helium for many years; and it was not until 1934, more than a quarter of a century after the first liquefaction of helium by Onnes using the Joule-Thomson effect, that the first successful piston-engine helium liquefier was devised by the Russian physicist Kapitza.[2]

[1] C. T. Lane, *Rev. Sci. Instr.*, **12**:326 (1941).
[2] P. L. Kapitza, *Proc. Roy. Soc. (London)*, **A147**:189 (1934).

The lubrication dilemma was evaded in a most ingenious way. The engine was arranged so that the travel of the piston was vertical, and the piston was "loosely" fitted in the cylinder. Actually, this gap was of the order of 10^{-3} in. In addition, the piston had a series of concentric grooves cut in it, each a few thousandths of an inch deep and wide. Upon admitting high-pressure gas to this engine, some escaped in the gap between piston and cylinder, but since the motion of the piston was rapid, this loss amounted, in practice, to only a few per cent and did not materially affect the engine's efficiency. And it was this leakage gas which created, by flowing around the grooves, a radial pressure on the piston which had the effect of requiring the axes of the piston and cylinder to be coincident as the condition for equilibrium.

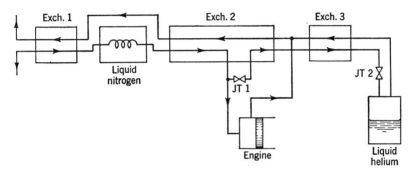

FIG. 8. Flow sheet for the Kapitza liquefier.

Thus, in a sense, the helium gas served as its own lubricant! Inspection of Fig. 7 shows that by starting the expansion at a low enough temperature (e.g., point 4), which might be produced by a heat exchanger ahead of the engine, we could, with a single expansion, proceed into the saturated region (point 5) and thus produce liquid directly in the engine, from which it could be drained.

In practice this is found to decrease sharply the efficiency of the engine, and hence a compromise is effected.[1] The engine is used strictly to refrigerate the gas, and final liquefaction is accomplished by Joule-Thomson expansion of part of the process gas.

Chemical engineers make use of "flow diagrams," which are analogous to the block diagrams used in electronics. Figure 8 is such a

---

[1] In Fig. 7 we have shown ideal conditions, i.e., expansion at constant entropy. In practice a certain amount of irreversibility is inevitable, and hence the entropy increases somewhat during the expansion. Nevertheless, modern helium engines have efficiencies of 70 to 80 per cent of an ideal reversible engine working between the same temperature limits.

diagram for the Kapitza liquefier.   The input pressure to the machine
is approximately 30 atm, and about 80 per cent of the process gas
passes through the single expansion engine.   The remaining 20 per
cent is admitted to the last (Joule-Thomson) heat exchanger, its
steady-state temperature being about 8°K.   However, as Fig. 5 shows,
30 atm at this temperature lies well off the Joule-Thomson inversion.
Hence the gas is reduced in pressure to about 15 atm by a throttling
valve (marked J.T.#1 in Fig. 8) prior to its admission to the last
exchanger.

The Kapitza design, the prototype of all later piston-engine lique-
fiers, was adopted by several other laboratories, notably the Institute
for Physical Problems in Moscow (Kapitza, 1938), Yale (Lane, 1941),
and the University of Munich (Meissner, 1942).   All these devices
were similar in design and performance.   With a gas flow rate of about
30 m³ STP per hour, the yield was about 1.5 liters/hr of liquid helium
with a start-up time of 1 to 2 hr.   After World War II a much better
version of the Kapitza machine, from the point of view of engineering
design, was introduced by Collins.   The version was put into commercial production by the A. D. Little Company of Cambridge,
Massachusetts, and is generally known as the "Collins cryostat."

The original Kapitza device was rather cranky in operation, so much
so that it needed "a physicist to run it."   The design also had several
important drawbacks including one very major one: its method of
thermal insulation, in which the liquefier proper (heat exchangers,
engine, etc.) was enclosed in a tank pumped to a high vacuum
($\sim 10^{-6}$ mm Hg).   This involved dozens of soldered joints; on one
side was helium gas at 30 atm pressure and on the other a very high
vacuum.   The leak potentialities were therefore enormous, and their
frequent occurrence involved lengthy shutdowns for detection and
repair.

Collins solved this cleverly by allowing the liquefier proper to be
surrounded with helium gas at about 1 atm pressure.   Thermal insulation is achieved by a large metal Dewar surrounding the whole.   Small
leaks are therefore unimportant.   There are numerous other improve-
ments which make the machine exceptionally reliable in operation; it
operates for months on end with the barest minimum of maintenance.

Two expansion engines, employed at different temperature levels,
are used in this design, and it is possible to liquefy helium without any
other source of refrigeration.   The yield under these circumstances is
not large, however, and it is found expedient to use liquid nitrogen as a
precoolant.   The machine then delivers from 4 to 6 liters/hr of liquid
helium; this improvement over the Kapitza prototype indicates a

much greater efficiency of engines and heat exchangers, despite the fact that the input pressure is only about half that used by Kapitza. It appears, in fact, that current models are not used to their full capacity. By employing more compressor capacity yields as high as 8 to 10 liters/hr have been achieved. There is no doubt that, from any angle, the Collins cryostat is the best helium liquefier extant.

HANDLING OF LIQUID HELIUM

Liquid helium, as delivered by the liquefier, is at a temperature of about 4.2°K. The latent heat is approximately ¾ g-cal/cm³—an extremely low figure compared to common liquids. At this temperature all other substances (except $_2$He^3) are solids, including, of course, air. Hence the liquid must be protected from the atmosphere at all times. The simple method for doing this consists in using a Dewar vessel which may be constructed of either glass or, less often, metal.

Because of the low latent heat of liquid helium, it is necessary to minimize the radiant-heat flow into the helium Dewar. This is done by surrounding the latter with a second Dewar containing liquid nitrogen (or air) so that the helium "looks at" approximately 77°K rather than the ambient room temperature. Current American practice is to make both Dewars of Pyrex glass. Apart from this, there are great variations in the shapes and dimensions of these containers; each setup is custom tailored to the problem at hand.

Very often both Dewars are cylindrical. Typical dimensions for the helium Dewar are 2 in. internal diameter and about 30 in. length; the shielding nitrogen Dewar is correspondingly larger, with an inner diameter typically 1.5 in. greater than the outer diameter of the helium vessel. The vacuum space in both is not critical, being generally of the order of ¼ in. or less. Both vessels are silvered except for a pair of longitudinal clear spaces on opposite ends of a diameter, running nearly the whole length of the Dewar. This clear strip is normally ⅜ to ½ in. wide and permits observation of the inside of the helium vessel. In all other respects, the nitrogen vessel is standard, its inner space being pumped to 10⁻⁶ mm Hg or thereabouts.

The helium Dewar, however, presents a more special case, since its contents must be shielded from the surrounding atmosphere; i.e., the interior of this vessel must be maintained "vacuumtight" at all times when containing liquid helium. The author's laboratory, over the years, has tried and discarded many designs. Our current device is sketched in Fig. 9 and consists of a Dewar built around a commercial flange produced by the Corning Glass Works, Corning, New York, for a different purpose,[1] namely, to couple lengths of glass pipe together into pipelines used by the chemical industry. These flanges are available in a variety of sizes, and we have made Dewars of up to 6 in. diam from them.

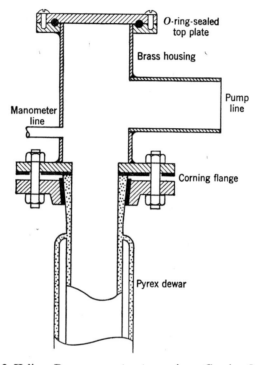

FIG. 9. Helium Dewar superstructure using a Corning flange.

The superstructure of the Dewar (Fig. 9), which remains at room temperature, is constructed of metal (usually brass), and the glass vessel bolts to it via the coupling and a neoprene gasket supplied with it. A metal pipe of the same diameter as the Dewar leads to a high-capacity vacuum pump so that the vapor pressure, and hence the temperature, of the helium bath may be controlled. The above system has been in use at Yale for several years and appears almost ideal from the viewpoint of ease of construction, maintenance, and reliability in operation.

It has been stated that the nitrogen-shield Dewar is standard and possesses an inner space pumped to high vacuum. This is not neces-

---

[1] This design originated at the Naval Research Laboratory, Washington, D.C., and I am indebted to Dr. R. T. Weber for it.

sary, or desirable, for the helium vessel.   Here the interspace has a very poor vacuum, of the order of 5 mm mercury pressure, the residual gas being air.   The purpose here is as follows.   In a given experiment, the helium Dewar contains various pieces of equipment whose aggregate mass may be a kilogram or more.   Initially the Dewar is evacuated and filled with helium gas at 1 atm pressure prior to admitting the liquid helium.   The Dewar and contents are thus initially at room temperature.   To cool this to 4.2°K would require a considerable amount of liquid helium because of the latter's low latent heat.   If, however, before the liquid helium is admitted, the helium Dewar and contents are permitted to sit for some minutes in the surrounding liquid-nitrogen bath, the residual air in the helium Dewar will act as a good heat conductor and the temperature of the whole will quickly reach 77°K.   If liquid helium is now admitted, the thermal load on the latter will be much reduced.   At the same time the residual air in the interspace will freeze, and the residual pressure will fall to the order of 10^{-10} mm mercury, i.e., a splendid insulating vacuum which lasts as long as there is any liquid helium in the Dewar.   Thus we have removed sensible heat with cheap liquid nitrogen rather than expensive liquid helium.   It is not too much to say that this trick, which appears to have originated at the Mond Laboratory, Cambridge, England, pretty nearly doubles the effective capacity of any helium liquefier.

Pyrex glass, which has the advantage of being readily available in a variety of sizes, has one drawback—it is somewhat permeable to helium gas at room temperature.   Thus, after repeated usage, the Dewars may go "soft" because of helium in the interspace.   This, however, is a minor inconvenience—the helium Dewar can be repumped after, say, each half-dozen runs.   Alternatively, if care is exercised never to fill the helium Dewar with gas unless it be at nitrogen temperature, the Dewars appear to last nearly indefinitely.

TEMPERATURE MEASUREMENT AND CONTROL

As is true for any pure liquid, the saturated vapor pressure of helium is a unique function of the temperature of the liquid.   The measurement of this pressure involves manometers which use either mercury or some low-vapor-pressure oil as the indicating liquid.   The corresponding temperature is determined by use of a constant-volume gas thermometer using helium gas at low pressure as the working substance.   Work of this kind, mainly carried out at Leiden, has been going on for many years, and from time to time, as new measurements are made, the pressure-temperature tables are revised and published. The latest of these, at the present writing, are reported by Van Dijk and Durieux[1] and cover the range from 0.9° to 5.22°K (the critical temperature) in steps of 0.01°K. For reference, these tables are called the L_{55} Scale. This excellent work therefore makes the precise measurement of the Kelvin temperature of a given batch of liquid easy; only some simple manometric measurements are required.

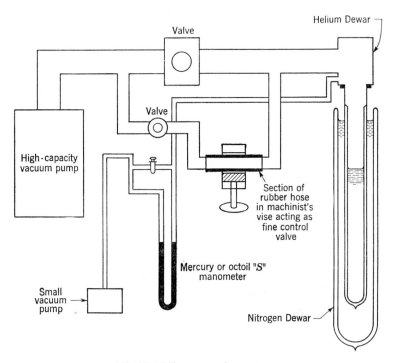

FIG. 10. Helium pumping system.

Figure 10 shows, via a block diagram, a typical arrangement for the control and measurement of temperature, using vapor-pressure manipulation. In many experiments the use of a secondary thermometer is necessary, which is almost always a resistance thermometer. Pure metals generally possess a temperature-independent resistivity in the liquid-helium region, but the situation with amorphous carbon and certain alloys is otherwise. A very simple thermometer, much used in American practice, consists of an ordinary carbon radio resistor. This

[1] H. Van Dijk and M. Durieux, "Progress in Low Temperature Physics," Interscience Publishers, Inc., New York, 1957, vol. II, p. 461.

has a semiconductor-type resistivity curve having a higher resistance at low temperatures than at room temperature. It must, of course, be calibrated by vapor-pressure measurements in liquid helium, and since they are not too reproducible from one run to the next, this is usually done simultaneously with the measurement in question.

MAGNETIC COOLING

The vapor pressure versus temperature curve for helium has been measured (by constant-volume gas thermometry) down to about 0.65°K, where it is approximately 10^{-3} mm mercury. The curve is roughly exponential and therefore permits us to estimate the value at, say, 0.2°K as around 10^{-15} mm mercury. It is clear, therefore, that the usual method of producing low temperatures, by pumping the vapor, ceases to be practical below about 0.7°K.

In 1926 Debye and Giauque, independently, suggested a new technique by means of which temperatures approaching a few microdegrees Kelvin have since been achieved. The method depends on the magneto-thermodynamic properties of a class of complex salts and, in principle, operates as follows (Fig. 11). The paramagnetic salt [e.g., chromium potassium alum $K_2SO_4 \cdot Cr_2(SO_4)_3 \cdot 24H_2O$] in the form of an ellipsoid of revolution is suspended by, e.g., nylon threads in a vacuumtight container. This is immersed in helium which is held at 1°K (lower if possible). This "salt pill" can be placed in the field of a powerful magnet (N-S) which can be removed from the vicinity of the cryostat as desired. A little He gas ("exchange gas") at a few microns pressure is admitted to the previously evacuated can and the magnetic field applied. The salt will derive energy from the magnetic field which, appearing as heat, will be conducted via the exchange gas to the helium bath at 1°K. After a few minutes the salt will find itself at 1°K in a magnetic field of, say, 10,000 gauss. The exchange gas is now removed, by pumping, until a high vacuum ($\sim 10^{-6}$ mm mercury) obtains in the can. The magnetic field is now removed, usually by sliding the magnet away from the cryostat. The salt now cools, practically instantaneously, to a temperature much lower than 1°K and, being thermally isolated to a high degree, slowly warms up, during a period of several hours or so, to the original 1°K.

All the salts used in this process obey, more or less exactly, what is known as Curie's law; i.e., the paramagnetic susceptibility χ is given by

$$\chi = \frac{\lambda}{T}$$

where T is the Kelvin temperature and λ is a constant for a given salt (Curie constant). In the case of chrome alum, for example, magnetic measurements above 1°K produce a value $\lambda = 3.73 \times 10^{-3}$, where the susceptibility is measured in emu per gram. Hence *if Curie's law con-*

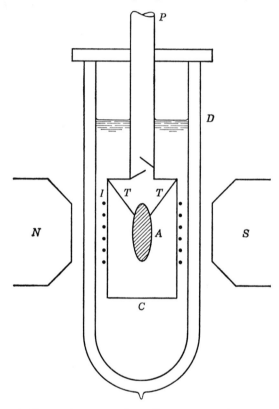

FIG. 11. Schematic illustrating magnetic cooling system. A, paramagnetic salt; C, vacuum can; D, Dewar (He at 1°K); NS, electromagnet; TT, insulating support; I, inductance coil; P, connection to vacuum pumps and exchange gas.

tinues valid below 1°K, the susceptibility at $T = 0.1$°K, for instance, would become

$$\chi_{0.1} = 3.73 \times 10^{-2} \quad \text{emu/g}$$

This is very large; the susceptibility of most common substances (non-ferromagnetics) at room temperature is of the order of 10^{-6} emu/g. Since the susceptibility and permeability (μ) are related via

$$\mu = 1 + 4\pi\chi$$
$$\mu \cong 1.5 \text{ at } 0.1°K$$

This value of permeability will substantially increase the induction in a small surrounding solenoid, and the change in its inductance so produced will be quite measurable. Hence we can measure, or better compare, the susceptibility of the salt at the lowest temperatures with the known values above 1°K very readily and thence, via the Curie law, find the temperature. The temperatures so determined are called "magnetic temperatures" and given the symbol T^*. T^* equals the Kelvin temperature if, and only if, Curie's law is obeyed below 1°K, a fact which remains to be proved.

The physics behind the method may be made clearer by the following simple qualitative argument. Each of the ions (Cr) in the salt possesses a magnetic moment, and the interactions between them are small because of the dilution of the chromium by other material. In other words, we have something approaching an ideal gas of magnetic particles. In a magnetic field these ions try to line up with their magnetic axes pointing in the field direction, this being the condition for minimum energy of the system. The tendency to alignment is opposed, however, by the thermal agitation of the ions which, of itself, tends to orient the magnetic axes randomly. The energy of an *aligned* dipole is[1]

$$\varepsilon_{mag} = -MH$$

where M is the magnetic moment. The thermal energy is, of course, of the order of kT (k = Boltzmann constant). Clearly, then, we get ever better alignment with the largest possible H and the smallest possible T. Applying elementary Boltzmann statistics to this problem, along the lines outlined above, we can readily show that gas must obey Curie's law for low H and high T.

Now we return to our salt at $T = 1°K$ and $H = 10,000$ gauss. The elementary magnets will be very substantially aligned; i.e., they will be

[1] Consider a magnet, pole strength m and moment $M = ml$, at an angle θ to a uniform field of strength H. Let the magnetic potential at the south pole (negative m) be P_0; then the potential at the north pole will be

$$P_0 - Hl \cos \theta$$

which is less since a unit positive pole would be urged in the direction of the field and so acquire kinetic energy in going from $-m$ to $+m$. The energy of the system would accordingly be

$$\varepsilon = -mP_0 + m(P_0 - Hl \cos \theta)$$
$$= -MH \cos \theta$$

Hence if the dipole were in its equilibrium position lying parallel to the field, its energy would be $-MH$, which is minimal as it should be.

highly ordered in the thermodynamic sense. Hence the "magnetic entropy" of the salt will be small, much smaller than it would be at the same temperature (1°K) *without* a field. If now we remove the field under conditions of high thermal isolation (i.e., adiabatic), this entropy may not change and the salt will find itself *with much smaller entropy than it had at 1°K*, both situations being in the *absence of a magnetic field*. But other things being equal, smaller entropy means lower temperature; hence the salt cools.

It must be emphasized, of course, that the entropy of these salts is composed of two parts:

1. A magnetic component due to unbalanced "electron spins," which we may call the magnetic entropy or spin entropy
2. The thermal entropy due to the ordinary specific heat or lattice waves, which we may call the lattice or thermal entropy

In order to cool the salt proper, we must remove this lattice entropy; i.e., there must be some sort of interaction between the spin system and lattice waves or "phonons." This will involve a "relaxation time," and in the early days of the subject it was feared that this would be exceedingly long—of the order of days. Thus it was feared that magnetic cooling might be illusory; in other words, we had produced a low "spin temperature," but being unable to communicate this to the lattice and hence to any other substance whose low-temperature properties we wished to measure, we had only an interesting stunt of no great practical use. Luckily the theoretical estimates of the spin-lattice relaxation times turned out to be quite false, and today we know that these are of the order of seconds at most.

The spin entropy versus temperature of a large number of these salts has been measured (by measuring specific heats), and a typical curve is sketched in Fig. 12, where the solid line is the entropy in *zero magnetic field* and the dots on the vertical line passing through 1°K are the entropies in various magnetic fields from 5 to 30 kilogauss. On this plot a line parallel to the abscissa would therefore represent a magnetic cooling experiment, and starting at 1°K and 10,000 gauss, for example, a final temperature of about 0.1°K would be reached with this particular salt. We note also the great desirability of starting the process at as low a bath temperature as possible. From Fig. 12 we notice also that, had we elected to start from 10°K, a field of the order of 150 kilogauss would be required to reach 0.1°K!

To many people entropy is a rather shadowy concept not easy to think about intuitively. In this respect energy and energy levels have a greater appeal; hence it is useful to regard the process of magnetic cooling in this light. The ions of the salt, in the absence of a magnetic field, occupy a set of very closely spaced, practically continuous energy levels, and the distribution of ions among these levels is given by a Boltzmann distribution. That is, the probability of finding an ion in an energy level ε_i is given by

$$e^{-\varepsilon_i/kT}$$

Thus if we *decrease* the ion's energy, the probability of finding it in the lower energy state *increases*. Now in a magnetic field the number of

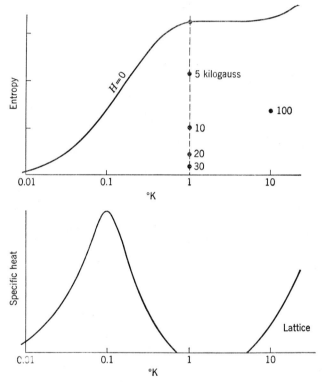

FIG. 12. Entropy and specific heat of a typical paramagnetic salt. The solid curve, in the upper figure, is the entropy in zero magnetic field; the dots are the entropies in the fields given. The specific-heat curve is for zero magnetic field.

ions whose moments tend to point in the direction of the field is greater than the number tending to point in the opposite direction, which fact leads to a positive magnetic susceptibility for the substance. Hence, in the field, the population of the lowest energy states will increase, since an ion with moment parallel has less energy $(-MH)$ than one antiparallel $(+MH)$. If now the field is removed without permitting any energy to enter or leave the system (i.e., adiabatically), the ions will find themselves with a higher population in the lowest levels than they would have had before the field was originally applied. This is another way of saying that the salt is at a lower temperature.

The first and second laws of thermodynamics may, for a magnetic substance, be written as

$$T\,dS = dU + P\,dV - H\,dM$$

Since we are dealing with solids whose expansion coefficient is small, we have

$$T\,dS = dU - H\,dM$$

Using the well-known thermodynamic relation,

$$T\,dS = C_H\,dT + T\left(\frac{\partial M}{\partial T}\right)_H dH$$

For an isentropic process $(dS = 0)$ we therefore get

$$\left(\frac{\partial T}{\partial H}\right)_S = -\frac{T}{C_H}\left(\frac{\partial M}{\partial T}\right)_H$$

where C_H is the specific heat of the substance in field H. Now since $(\partial M/\partial T)_H$ is negative for Curie's law, $(\partial T/\partial H)_S$ is positive, which means a decrease in T for a decrease in H provided the process takes place at constant entropy.

For a Curie's-law substance

$$\frac{M}{H} = \chi = \frac{\lambda}{T}$$
$$C \sim T^3$$

that is,

$$\left(\frac{\partial T}{\partial H}\right)_S \sim \frac{H}{T^4}$$

which means that, although there will be some cooling at any temperature, it will be really large only at the lowest temperatures, which is just what we require.

There is one property of these salts which, although it was unknown when the method was proposed, has turned out to be of paramount practical importance. This is generally referred to as the "specific-heat anomaly." At temperatures below 1°K the specific heat "peaks" to a large value at some low temperature, which is different for different salts. Were it not for this fortunate fact, the magnetic cooling method would be of only marginal and transitory interest.

The reason for this lies in the fact that, in order to be useful, it is necessary to maintain the low temperatures against the inevitable heat leaks into the apparatus for a time sufficient to perform the desired measurements.   Further, if it is desired to cool some other substance (liquid helium, for example) to the low temperatures achieved by the salt, a large specific heat in the latter is desirable and necessary.

It remains for us to inquire as to the validity of Curie's law in the region below 1°K or, said another way, to determine the relationship between the magnetic and true Kelvin temperatures.   The actual determination of the relationship between the two constitutes one of the cleverest applications of thermodynamics extant and is due principally to F. Simon and N. Kurti.

DETERMINATION OF $T^* = \varphi(T)$

The experiment consists of two parts:[1]

1. Starting at a fixed (Kelvin) temperature which is known by vapor-pressure measurements ($\sim$1°K), we perform a series of demagnetizations from different initial fields to zero field.   In each case we measure the T^* temperature.

2. We determine the specific heat at these T^* temperatures ($C^*_{H=0}$), using a constant heat source (γ rays) which we calibrate by making observations above 1°K, where the specific heat is known from calorimetric measurements.

Figure 13 shows, schematically, an isentropic line ($dS = 0$) on a temperature versus field plot for the salt being tested.   Clearly,

$$S_1 = S_3 \tag{12}$$

Hence
$$S_2 - S_1 = S_2 - S_3 \tag{13}$$

Also
$$T \, dS = dU - H \, dM \tag{14}$$

Also
$$\chi = \frac{M}{H} = \frac{\lambda}{T} \qquad \text{per unit vol}$$

But
$$S_2 - S_1 = \int_2^1 dS \qquad \text{at const } T_0 \text{ (i.e., } dU = 0)$$

whence
$$T_0(S_1 - S_2) = - \int_0^{H_i} H \, dM = - \int_0^{H_i} \frac{\lambda H \, dH}{T_0}$$

that is,
$$S_2 - S_1 = \frac{\lambda}{2} \left(\frac{H_i}{T_0} \right)^2$$

---

[1] In what follows it must constantly be borne in mind that the Kelvin or absolute temperature is defined through, and only through, the second law of thermodynamics.

Since all quantities on the right-hand side of the above equation are known, $S_2 - S_1$ is known.

If we perform this experiment a number of times, each with a different value of H_i (and always from temperature T_0), and at the same time measure T^* at each zero field point, we get $S_2 - S_3 = S_2 - S_1$ as a function of T^*. Since, further, S_2 is constant, we can plot S_3 as a

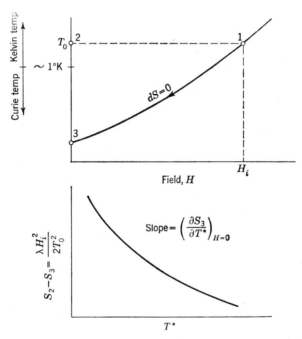

FIG. 13. The process of determining Curie temperatures in terms of Kelvin temperatures.

function of T^*. This is indicated in Fig. 13. Hence we have experimentally determined the quantity $(\partial S_3/\partial T^*)_{H=0}$ as a function of T^*. Now, when $H = 0$,

$$T\, dS = dU$$

that is,

$$T = \left(\frac{\partial U}{\partial S}\right)_{H=0}$$

which may be written

$$T = \left(\frac{\partial U}{\partial S}\right)_{H=0} = \frac{(\partial U/\partial T^*)_{H=0}}{(\partial S/\partial T^*)_{H=0}} = \frac{C^*_{H=0}}{(\partial S/\partial T^*)_{H=0}}$$

This equation thus gives us the Kelvin temperature T as a function of T^* provided we can measure $C^*_{H=0}$ (the specific heat in zero field at the lowest temperatures) as a function of T^*.   To do this, we provide a γ-ray source outside the cryostat and observe T^* (by susceptibility measurements) when the sample is irradiated for a predetermined fixed time τ, whence

$$C^*_{H=0} = \left(\frac{\Delta Q}{\Delta T^*} \right)_{H=0}$$

In order to determine ΔQ, we make a similar measurement above $\sim 1°$K, where C is known from ordinary calorimetric measurements. This is legitimate since ΔQ will depend only on the effective strength of the γ-ray source, the time interval of irradiation τ, and the (fixed) geometry of the apparatus.   Thus we have T as a function of T^*.   A typical result is shown in Fig. 14.

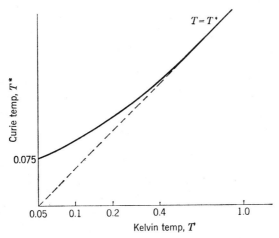

FIG. 14. Experimentally determined relation between the Curie and Kelvin temperatures for potassium chrome alum. [*Bleaney, Proc. Roy. Soc. (London)*, A204:216 (1950).]

The magnetic cooling method has been applied to a great variety of investigations in low-temperature physics.   Usually when, for instance, the properties of liquid helium itself at the lowest temperatures are under investigation, the experimental chamber is hung from the salt by means of a copper rod.   The salt is usually molded around the rod, which possesses copper fins to assure a large area for thermal contact.   Regrettably, the thermal conductivity of these salts is small, so heat-exchange problems are troublesome in this sort of work.

The ellipsoidal shape for the salt used in our illustration is desirable since, because of the large permeability, demagnetizing (i.e., shape) effects have to be allowed for in making the magnetic temperature measurements. Very often, however, for technical simplicity, a long cylindrical shape is used and appropriate corrections made.

For most work down to 0.1°K the Curie and Kelvin temperatures are sufficiently close so that no attempt is made to calibrate the salt used in a given experiment. This has some elements of danger in it, of course, but it is a very general practice in modern work.

He³ REFRIGERATORS

In the last 5 years the growing availability of pure isotope He³ has led to the widespread use of a second technique for producing deep temperatures. This depends on the fact that the vapor pressure of this isotope is much higher, at a given temperature, than that of He⁴. For example, at 1°K liquid He³ (normal boiling point 3.2°K) has a saturated vapor pressure some eighty times larger than He⁴. Consequently, quite ordinary pumps are able to maintain temperatures as low as 0.4 to 0.5°K in a properly shielded bath of this liquid.

The difficulty with the method is strictly economic, since the gas required to produce about 1.5 cm³ of liquid costs in the neighborhood of $1,500. Hence the system must be completely tight, with the efflux gas from the pump being preserved and recycled. For refrigeration and shielding, of course, ordinary liquid helium is employed.

The He³ and magnetic cycles are sometimes teamed up. It will have been clear from our discussion of the magnetic cooling technique that the "figure of merit" is the ratio $(H/T)_{initial}$, which should be as large as possible. Since 100-kilogauss magnets are extremely expensive propositions, we can do better by making $T_{initial}$ as low as possible. Thus with the He³ stage and using a 10- to 15-kilogauss magnet, temperatures of the order of 10 millidegrees are obtainable. There is, however, an additional piece of equipment involved in this, namely, the "heat switch." This device connects the salt to the He³ bath and, during magnetization, must be a good thermal conductor to remove the magnetic entropy. But during the demagnetization stage it must be quite the reverse, namely, a very poor heat conductor.

There are various ways of accomplishing this; one of the neatest is the use of a Pb wire. This material has the property that in the presence of a magnetic field of about 1,000 gauss or more it has a high thermal conductance, whereas for fields less than about this figure its conductance becomes orders of magnitude less. As will be realized, this is precisely what we require of a heat switch; further, its mode of operation ties in nicely with our magnetic cooling technique.

CHAPTER 2

Helium II

THE λ POINT

About 1927 Keesom and Wolfke at Leiden measured the dielectric constant of liquid helium as a function of temperature. They found a small apparent discontinuity in the curve at a temperature in the vicinity of 2.2°K. It was suggested that liquid helium at that temperature undergoes some sort of transformation.

What we call transformations are fairly common phenomena and are classed, thermodynamically, as two types: first-order (with a latent heat) and second-order (no latent heat). A common first-order transition occurs when a saturated vapor condenses into a liquid phase; a typical second-order one is the transformation from ferro- to paramagnetism when a piece of iron is heated through its Curie temperature. In both these examples (there are many others) there occurs a jump in the specific heat at the transition temperature in question.

Accordingly, Keesom and coworkers around 1932 made some careful measurements of the specific heat versus temperature curve for liquid helium. The result (Fig. 15) indeed showed the expected jump at about the same temperature as the observed discontinuity in the dielectric constant. At the same time, a careful search for an accompanying latent heat showed it to be less than 2×10^{-3} cal/g; i.e., the transition was second-order. Also at the same time, a rather more exact determination of the transition temperature showed it to occur at a helium vapor pressure of 38.3 mm mercury, corresponding to a temperature of 2.186°K on the then available temperature scale. The similarity of the shape of the specific-heat curve to the Greek letter "lambda" caused Keesom to name the transition the "λ point," a terminology which is now universally adopted. In addition, the temperature region above the λ point was designated as helium I (He I); that below, helium II (He II). It was, of course, quite unknown at the time whether or not He I and He II differed in their properties in any important way.

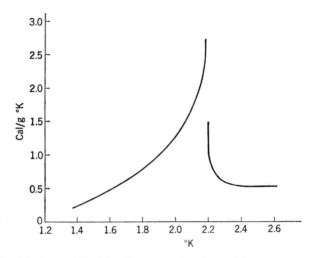

FIG. 15. Specific heat of liquid helium as a function of temperature. (*Keesom*, 1932.)

However, a rather isolated observation made at the University of Toronto by McLennan and coworkers, at about this same time (1932), foreshadowed things to come. It was observed that upon cooling the helium through the λ point, a dramatic change in the appearance of the liquid occurred. He I, like any familiar liquid, boiled with fine bubbles, but He II showed no traces of bubbles of any kind. We now know that this effect, familiar to all low-temperature physicists, is due to the very different mechanism of heat conduction in the two phases.

The most recent work on the lambda transition[1] has measured the specific heat at temperatures as close as 10 microdegrees to the singularity. There is a discontinuity in the specific heat amounting to 5.6 joules/g°K; the specific heat immediately above the λ point is less

[1] W. M. Fairbank, M. J. Buckingham, and C. F. Kellers, Fifth International Conference on Low Temperature Physics and Chemistry, Madison, Wisconsin, 1957.

by this amount than that immediately below.   The specific heat does not, however, become infinite as some earlier workers had sometimes supposed on the basis of the less well-resolved data (Fig. 15) of Keesom.

THE FOUNTAIN EFFECT

In the early thirties only two laboratories interested in physics and capable of producing liquid helium in quantity were in existence. These were at Leiden and Toronto.   Around 1936 three powerful

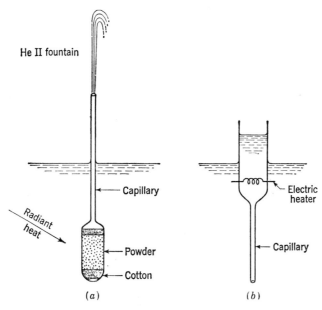

FIG. 16. Two variations of the "fountain-effect" experiment.   (*Allen and Jones,* 1938.)

units were added, each capable of producing liquid helium in quantity and each with the know-how to use it.   These were at Oxford and Cambridge in England and the Institute for Physical Problems in Moscow.   The results of these additions were felt almost at once.[1]

Although the term "breakthrough" is hackneyed and much beloved of politicians, still it aptly describes a discovery made, almost by accident, by Allen and Jones at Cambridge in 1938.[2]   Figure 16 shows two variations of the experiment.   Figure 16a shows a glass capillary

[1] At the present writing there are about 100 such laboratories throughout the world.

[2] J. F. Allen and H. Jones, *Nature,* **141**:243 (1938).

with an enlarged end which is packed tightly with a fine powder. Both ends of the glass tube are open, and the powder end is immersed in He II as shown. When radiant heat from a source outside the cryostat is permitted to fall on the powder, a liquid-helium fountain as high as several centimeters emerges from the capillary. It need scarcely be said that the effect occurs only for He II—never for He I.

Figure 16b shows a less spectacular but rather more useful variation. Here the heat is supplied electrically (in milliwatt amounts), and a static level difference between the liquid in the tube and the outside bath is produced. This pressure difference is a function of the power supplied and also of the ambient temperature. As later measurements will show, it is accurately proportional to the temperature difference between the liquid in the tube and the bath.

MECHANO-CALORIC EFFECT

An experiment closely related to the fountain effect (it is sometimes called the inverse of it) was performed by Daunt and Mendelssohn in 1939.[1] This arrangement is sketched in Fig. 17. Here a small Dewar is open at the bottom end and contains, at this point, a plug of fine emery powder. The vessel contains also an electrical resistance thermometer using, in accordance with European practice, a fine wire of copper-tin-lead alloy (phosphor bronze). Arrangements are provided such that the vessel may be lowered into a bath of He II or, alternatively, withdrawn. Thus liquid flows either into the bulb or out of it. When liquid flows *into* the bulb, a *decrease* in the temperature, of the order of 10^{-2}°K, is observed on the resistance thermometer. When liquid flows out of the vessel, an increase in temperature of the same amount occurs.

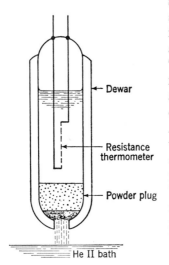

FIG. 17. Mechano-caloric effect. (*Daunt and Mendelssohn, 1939.*)

We may sum up the situation presented by these two experiments by saying that sources of heat in He II produce motion of the liquid and, conversely, a motion of the liquid produces temperature differences. These experiments alerted physicists to the fact

[1] J. G. Daunt and K. Mendelssohn, *Nature*, **143**:719 (1939).

that in He II they were dealing with an exceedingly strange liquid, one unique, in fact, in human experience. And Keesom's somewhat optimistic classification of liquid helium into states I and II was brilliantly justified.

VISCOSITY

Now in 1939 the physics of liquids was an old and, we supposed, well-established branch. Although no respectable molecular theory of liquids existed, as it hardly does today, still more than a

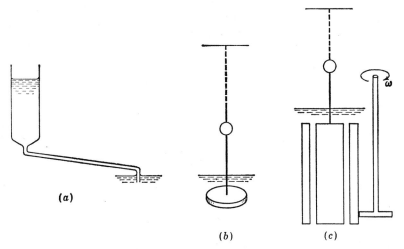

FIG. 18. Three types of viscosimeters used for liquid helium: (*a*) Poiseuille flow; (*b*) oscillating disc; (*c*) concentric cylinder.

century of hydrodynamics had gone by with a host of experimental techniques for the study of the liquid state. In particular, several time-tested methods for determining the viscosity of simple liquids were at hand. Hence several laboratories set about measuring the viscosity of He II, and, as luck would have it, they each employed different, though equally respectable, methods.

We shall not, at this point, dwell upon these early experiments in any detail, but rather shall get on with the results. In classical hydrodynamics there are three oft-used methods for absolute-viscosity studies, as follows (Fig. 18):

1. Poiseuille's Method. This depends on measuring the volume rate of flow ($\dot{V}$) of liquid in a narrow channel under a steady pressure gradient. Usually the channel is a capillary of circular cross section, and if the flow is nonturbulent, then

$$\dot{V} = \frac{\pi a^4}{8\eta} \frac{p_1 - p_2}{l} \qquad \text{cm}^3/\text{sec} \qquad (1)$$

where a = radius of capillary

p_1, p_2 = pressure at distance l apart

η = viscosity coefficient

Thus the average velocity of flow is directly proportional to the hydrostatic pressure difference which produces it. If the flow is turbulent, the velocity goes as the square root of the pressure.

2. Oscillating Disc. Here a thin circular disc is suspended, via a torsion fiber, and given simple harmonic oscillations about an axis perpendicular to the plane of the disc through the center. The oscillations of the disc, when totally immersed in the liquid, suffer a damping which depends on the product of the viscosity and density of the surrounding liquid.

3. Concentric Cylinder Viscometer. A hollow cylinder surrounds a concentric inner cylinder, the latter hung from a torsion fiber. The gap between the two cylinders is the order of a millimeter or so and is filled with the liquid under test. The outer cylinder is rotated at constant angular velocity, whereupon the inner experiences a torque, measured by the deflection of the fiber, which is proportional to the product of the viscosity and the angular velocity of the outer cylinder, ω, i.e.,

$$\text{Torque} = 4\pi\eta L \frac{a_1{}^2 a_2{}^2}{a_2{}^2 - a_1{}^2} \omega$$

Here a_2 and a_1 are the radii of the outer and inner cylinders and L is their length.

It will be observed that methods 1 and 3 yield the viscosity coefficient directly; in method 2 it is necessary also to determine the density ρ of the fluid. With any "classical" liquid (e.g., water or He I) all three methods yield the same answer for η within the experimental error.

But the early workers using methods 1 and 2 (method 3 was not used for liquid helium until much later) found alarmingly different values for η in He II. Thus Kapitza and others found that He II flowed through even the narrowest channel (width the order of 0.1 μ) with great ease even under quite tiny pressure heads (order of 100 dynes/cm^2). Worse still, Allen and Misener found that for such narrow channels the flow was quite independent of the pressure head Δp. We recall that for laminar flow a viscous liquid should go as Δp and for turbulent flow as $\sqrt{\Delta p}$. It appeared, in fact, that as determined by method 1 the viscosity of He II was vanishingly small, possibly zero! With method 2, however, the same He II at the same temperature produced a damping of the disc's motion which, however, decreased sharply as the temperature decreased from the λ point. The specific gravity of He II is closely temperature independent and has a value of about ⅛. Using this value, the viscosity as deduced from the observed damping turned out to be quite finite, of the order of at least a million times greater than that determined by method 1! Here, then, was a proper dilemma—two time-tested and, we thought, reliable methods of measuring viscosity giving values which were poles apart.

KAPITZA'S EXPERIMENT

Before discussing plausible explanations of these odd effects, it is well to consider an experiment performed by Kapitza in 1941.[1]

Figure 19 is a much simplified sketch of Kapitza's apparatus which, however, conveys the essential ideas. A glass Dewar A (not silvered) contained a sidearm tube which terminated in a pair of optical quartz flats S_1 and S_2. These made a fine annular slit through which liquid could enter or leave vessel A. By pressing the flats more tightly together, the width of the channel could be altered. The gap between S_1 and S_2 could be determined (when immersed in liquid helium) by observing interference fringes produced by monochromatic light.

Sealed into bulb A was an electric heating coil H plus a phosphor-bronze resistance thermometer T_1. The bulb could be raised or lowered in the surrounding helium bath, which contained a second thermometer T_2. The sensitivity of these thermometers was such that temperature differences of less than 10^{-4}°K could be detected.

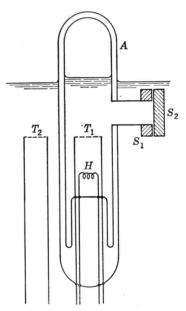

FIG. 19. Kapitza's 1941 experiment; a simplified version of his apparatus is illustrated.

Upon immersing the empty bulb in the He II bath so that the slit

[1] P. Kapitza, *J. Phys. (U.S.S.R.)*, **5**:59 (1941).

was beneath the surface, liquid flowed into the bulb until the levels inside and outside coincided. Thermometer T_1 showed a cooling effect, thus substantiating the previously discovered mechano-caloric effect. If now a certain electric current was supplied to H, the liquid in the bulb rose steadily above the bath level until an equilibrium height was established (fountain effect). The equilibrium pressure difference Δp was found to be a linear function of the difference in

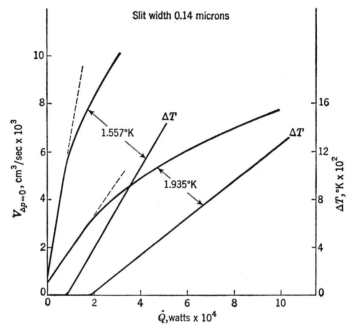

FIG. 20. Kapitza's experiment.

temperature ΔT between the liquid in the bulb and bath, at any given ambient temperature. The slope $\Delta p/\Delta T$ decreased with decreasing ambient temperature but was independent of slit width within wide limits.

The Dewar bulb is not, of course, completely adiabatic. It loses heat via a combination of radiation into the cooler bath plus ordinary conduction through the electric leads. At the fountain-pressure equilibrium the amount of heat entering (via H) and leaving the bulb via losses must, of course, be equal. Actually, with no current in the heater, the liquid in the bulb will be a little warmer than that of the bath because of stray radiation from outside the cryostat, resulting in a slight fountain pressure. This effect was, in Kapitza's apparatus, very small.

Kapitza's main contribution, in this paper, consisted of studying the "dynamic" fountain effect as opposed to the above-discussed static effect. That is to say, he measured the volume rate of flow of liquid into the bulb, $\dot{V}$ (as a function of rate of flow of heat into it), extrapolated to zero pressure difference. Since the cross-sectional area of the bulb was uniform and known, he needed only to measure the *initial* rate of rise of the bulb liquid level as a function of heat input $\dot{Q}$ (calories per second). At the same time he could also measure the temperature difference $\Delta T = T_1 - T_2$. Figure 20 shows some typical results, wherein both the flow rate $\dot{V}_{\Delta p=0}$ and ΔT are plotted against $\dot{Q}$.

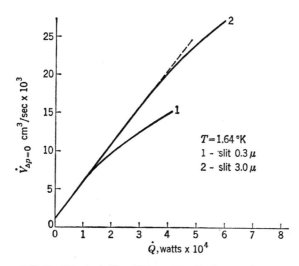

FIG. 21. Effect of slit width on Kapitza's experiment.

We observe that $\dot{V}_{\Delta p=0}$ has a linear portion followed by a nonlinear one and that $\Delta T = 0$, within the limits of accuracy, during the linear part of the curve but increases thereafter. Kapitza's interpretation of these curious results was as follows. The heat content of the bulk He II (in bath or bulb) is different from the heat content of the helium flowing in the narrow slit. More exactly, the heat content of helium found in narrow channels is *less* than that of helium in bulk, but this is true only up to a certain "critical" velocity of flow through the slit corresponding to the point of departure of the curve from linearity. In this connection Fig. 21 shows the effect of varying the slit width by a factor of 10; for the wider slit the linear portion (in which $\Delta T = 0$) extends to higher values of $\dot{V}_{\Delta p=0}$.

This postulated "difference in heat content" amounting to q cal/g of liquid He II is readily calculated in the linear region as

$$q = \frac{\dot{Q}}{\rho \dot{V}_{\Delta p=0}}$$

where ρ is the density of the helium. The values of this q, as derived from the data, turn out to be independent of the slit width for slits ranging from 0.3 to 3.0 μ. They are, however, temperature dependent, as Fig. 22 shows.

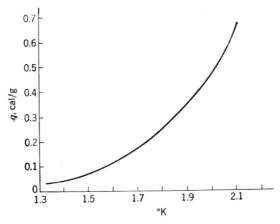

FIG. 22. q values as a function of temperature. (*Kapitza*, 1941.)

We have now discussed four fundamental and pioneer experiments, all of which show that He II is a very oddly behaving fluid indeed. The acute observer will have noticed that nearly all of these experiments involve narrow channels of one kind or another, i.e., capillaries, powder-packed tubes, and optical flats in close contact. Thus it would appear that He II confined to a narrow space is somehow a different kind of substance from helium in bulk. Kapitza had shown one difference, namely, a difference in heat content; but he had not the advantage of knowing a model for He II which several theoreticians had proposed by the time of his experiments. We now proceed to introduce this "two fluid" hypothesis.

Before we leave this discussion, however, it is amusing to recall a different kind of experiment, also performed about this same time by

Kapitza. It was mostly a qualitative experiment and had several variations; two of these arrangements are sketched in Fig. 22a.

On the left side we have a hollow glass "spider" which is free to rotate on a needle-point bearing; the whole is immersed in He II. When the liquid inside the bulb was heated (via external radiation), the spider rotated about its vertical axis of support. (A rather similarly shaped device is commonly used in a lawn sprinkler.) Clearly, liquid was being forced out of the jets, and the resulting reaction force on the spider produced the rotational torque. But this was accompanied by a startling effect; namely, the rotation continued indefinitely, and the interior of the bulb remained always full of liquid. We remark, in

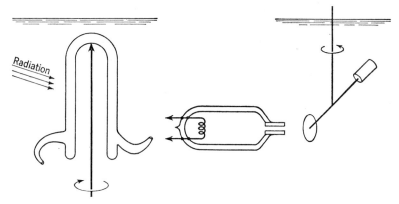

FIG. 22a. Kapitza's experiment on heat-induced motion in He II.

passing, that the glass of the bulb was quite impervious to He II. The only way liquid could get in (or out) of the bulb was via the spider arms.

In the second variation the bulb consists of a small Dewar vessel with a sealed-in electric heating coil. This bulb is open to the helium bath via a capillary neck whose diameter is the order of a millimeter. Near the neck is a light vane, as shown, hung from a torsion fiber. When a little heat was applied, the vane deflected, showing that there was a steady efflux of liquid from the vessel. But, as before, the bulb never emptied!

By using very small vanes, Kapitza studied the topology of the effluent jet. He found it very well defined, about the same diameter as the capillary; and it preserved its cross section, out into the bath, to a distance many times the diameter of the capillary.

At the time of the experiment (1942) Kapitza advanced the only explanation of this strange phenomenon which appeared at all plausible.   He supposed that there were *two* streams of fluid involved, one into and the other out of the opening, each transporting the same amount of mass per second.   Kapitza assumed further that in order to keep the two flows from interfering with one another inside the capillary, the ingoing stream was confined to a very narrow region in the vicinity of the capillary wall.   Hence the outgoing stream would occupy the bulk of the capillary's cross section.

In the light of our present knowledge this explanation is nearly, but not quite, the correct one, as will emerge in due course.

CHAPTER 3

The Two-fluid Model
of He II

FUNDAMENTAL POSTULATES

In the late thirties, a possible model for He II in which it was envisaged as a sort of "mixture" of two fluids, each possessing separate properties, must have occurred to many people, experimentalists and theoreticians alike. But F. London and L. Tisza on one hand and L. Landau on the other arrived at and published, quite independently, theories which were quite similar in many respects.

One of the most striking features of liquid helium is the fact that, to the best of our knowledge, it exists as a liquid down to absolute zero. This is a consequence of two things: (1) the van der Waals forces in helium are weak; (2) the zero-point energy, in consequence of the light mass, is large. The atoms in the liquid are, in consequence, relatively far apart, and it requires considerable pressure (about 26 atm at $0°K$) to force them into the solid configuration. No other substance (except the isotope He^3) acts thus. Hence helium is unique, owing to this interplay of quantum effects, and is often called, in the literature, a quantum liquid.

We shall start by making a number of unproved assumptions about He II, as follows:

1. The energy spectrum is such that He II consists of a "background" phase (superfluid) plus an excited (higher-energy) phase

(normal fluid). At absolute zero the entire liquid is superfluid; as the temperature is raised, excitations appear, the density of which depends only on temperature. Formally we can describe these two phases by densities ρ_s and ρ_n; the subscripts refer to superfluid phase and normal phase, respectively. If the "ordinary" density of the liquid is ρ, then

$$\rho_s + \rho_n = \rho$$

Also $\qquad\qquad \rho_s = \rho \qquad \rho_n = 0 \qquad T = 0°\text{K}$

$$\rho_s = 0 \qquad \rho_n = \rho \qquad T = \lambda \text{ point } (T_\lambda)$$

Apart from these limits, the exact form of ρ_n/ρ or ρ_s/ρ as a function of temperature remains, at the moment, undetermined.

2. The viscosity of the superfluid is zero. It is also energetically at absolute zero; i.e., its entropy is also zero. Contrariwise, the normal fluid possesses both viscosity and entropy.

3. The fact that $\rho_n/\rho = 1 - \rho_s/\rho$ is a function of the temperature leads rather naturally to the following picture. Suppose, in a mass of He II all at one temperature, the temperature at some point is suddenly raised. This creates more excitations; i.e., ρ_n/ρ increases while ρ_s/ρ decreases at this point. Thus a "density fluctuation" is created, and we should expect the liquid to try to restore the equilibrium by the flow of superfluid from the surrounding liquid to the warmer point. In order to conserve mass, a balancing flow of normal fluid away from the point must occur. In accordance with postulate 2, this process, termed "internal convection" by F. London, should be a powerful means of transferring heat because all the entropy of He II lies in the normal fluid—the superfluid has none. The normal fluid streaming away from the hot spot will carry entropy (i.e., heat) away, and in comparatively large amounts.

These postulates appear relatively simple but also somewhat surprising. There is, however, overwhelming evidence, as will emerge, for believing them essentially correct and necessary to any theory of He II.

Postulate 2 at once removes the viscosity measurements mystery discussed in Chap. 2. In the capillary the flow we observe is due to the superfluid, whose viscosity is zero. The normal component, possessing viscosity, can scarcely flow through the narrow tube. The measurement thus yields zero viscosity as it should. For the oscillating disc or rotating cylinder, however, the situation is reversed. The superfluid, possessing no viscosity, exerts no force on the solid bodies—only the normal component does so. This measurement thus yields the finite normal-component viscosity as it should.

Again in Kapitza's dynamic fountain-effect measurements, the liquid flowing through the slit is indeed different from the bulk liquid. The liquid flowing through the narrow channel is superfluid, practically exclusively, since the viscosity of the normal component precludes any appreciable flow. The q values represent the difference in energy between superfluid and the mixture of superfluid and normal fluid at the ambient temperature, which we call the bulk liquid. If we divide the q values given in Fig. 22 by the absolute temperature, we obtain, of course, the difference in the specific entropy between bulk and superfluid. Now the entropy of the bulk liquid can be obtained from the specific-heat measurements. When these two determinations of the entropy are compared, they are found to agree rather accurately. The only inference we can accordingly draw is that the entropy of the superfluid is zero, as was assumed in postulate 2. The helium fountain is a consequence of (3) above, since the fountain is pure superfluid.

The superfluid, possessing no viscosity, flows quite frictionlessly through pipes and past solid objects, ignoring also the normal-component excitations since the collision cross section of its atoms is, like the ideal gas, zero. But these atoms, being helium atoms, possess mass and are subject to gravitational attraction. Thus, in the static fountain effect, at equilibrium the thermal diffusion force postulated in (3) is balanced by the gravitational pressure head. This frictionless aspect of the superfluid would lead us to suspect that the fountain effect and the mechano-caloric effects are, thermodynamically speaking, reversible. We must now account for the mechano-caloric effect. The liquid entering (or leaving) the bulb is practically pure superfluid because of the filtering action of the narrow channels formed by the pressed powder. Thus, owing to postulate 2, no entropy either enters or leaves the bulb. The mass of liquid in the bulb, however, either increases or decreases, and thus the *specific* entropy of the fluid in the bulb decreases on filling or increases on emptying. A decrease or increase in the specific entropy of a system, otherwise isolated, leads, as we know, to a corresponding decrease or increase in temperature. This is what is observed. Alternatively, we can consider the process in this manner. Thus, on emptying the vessel, only superfluid flows out. Thus the ratio $\rho_n/\rho = 1 - \rho_s/\rho$ of the liquid remaining in the vessel *increases*. Hence the temperature must increase according to postulate 1.

We see, therefore, that the above postulates account very nicely for all the experimental findings we have so far chosen to present. Using ideas very similar to these, H. London in 1939[1] deduced a celebrated

[1] H. London, *Proc. Roy. Soc. (London)*, **A171**:484 (1939).

formula for the static fountain effect which we now proceed to prove. The proof involves the assumption that the process is thermodynamically reversible, which, owing to the frictionless nature of the superfluid, is certainly plausible.

H. LONDON'S THEOREM

Consider two volumes A and B (Fig. 23) connected by so fine a capillary that only the superfluid may flow through it. Both A and B are, initially, at the same temperature T. We suppose that this system is adiabatically isolated, except that a certain definite amount of heat energy may be supplied at will to B and a certain amount may be removed from A.

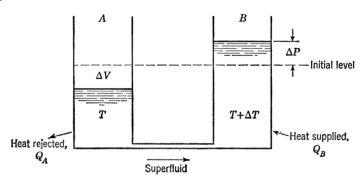

FIG. 23. Illustrating the derivation of the fountain-pressure formula. (*H. London*, 1939.)

Suppose we supply a finite amount of heat, Q_B, to B. This will raise the temperature of the helium in B from ambient T to $(T + \Delta T)$. By postulate 3 superfluid will flow (say m grams) from A to B, creating a small pressure head ΔP as shown. The loss of m grams of superfluid from A will, however, tend to increase the temperature of the liquid in A above the initial ambient temperature T. To maintain A at temperature T we must, therefore, remove a definite quantity of heat, Q_A, from it.

In transporting m grams of helium in the superfluid state from A to B we must do work[1] against the gravitational pressure head ΔP, which is (see Fig. 23)

$$W = \Delta P \, \Delta V = \Delta P \, \frac{m}{\rho} \tag{1}$$

[1] Since the fluid which flows from A to B is frictionless, this is the only mechanical work done.

where ρ is the weight density of liquid helium which, as we have remarked, is the same for both normal and superfluid. Also, by conservation of energy,

$$Q_B - Q_A = \Delta P \frac{m}{\rho} \qquad (2)$$

Let us denote the entropy per gram of He II, at the temperature T, by S. By postulate 2 this is also the entropy of the normal fraction of the mixture; the superfluid fraction possesses none. The heat which we must remove from A must accordingly be

$$Q_A = mST \qquad (3)$$

and that supplied at B will be

$$Q_B = mS(T + \Delta T) \qquad (4)$$

All this provided the process is thermodynamically reversible and ΔT is infinitesimal.

Physically, the meaning of Eq. (4) [or Eq. (3)] may be seen as follows. The m grams of pure superfluid entering B is, energetically, at absolute zero. A certain fraction of it, appropriate to the temperature a shade above T in B, must be converted to the normal state. Said differently, the entropy of the m grams must be raised from zero to the entropy value which the m grams would possess at the finite temperature T. This is S, the entropy per gram of liquid helium at temperature T.

Combining Eqs. (2) to (4), we then get

$$\Delta P = \rho S \, \Delta T \qquad (5)$$

This is H. London's equation, which has been tested, experimentally, over a wide range of temperatures by several investigators and has been found to be accurate. Since the measurement is relatively simple technically, it provides a nice method of determining the entropy of He II as a function of temperature. This, when compared with the calorimetric values, provides a most convincing proof of the correctness of the two-fluid hypothesis.

Since the density ρ of He II is closely temperature independent, a glance at the fountain-pressure measurements of Kapitza (Fig. 24) will show that the specific entropy of He II is much larger near the λ point than at the lower temperatures. This is largely due to the fact that the normal-fluid fraction steadily decreases as the temperature is decreased below the λ transition.

THE NAVIER-STOKES EQUATION

The equation of motion of a classical viscous fluid is one of the cornerstones of hydrodynamics, and we might guess, in the light of our discussion up to this point, that it would be applicable to the normal-fluid component. Actually, as we shall see, it requires some modification in view of the fountain effect, but in many instances it is

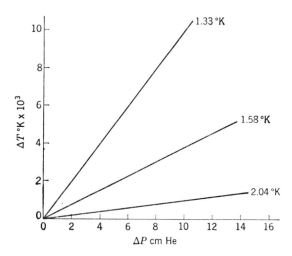

FIG. 24. Fountain effect showing the linear relation between ΔP and ΔT. (*Kapitza,* 1941.)

a sufficiently good approximation to be useful. This equation, called by many authors the "Navier-Stokes," reads as follows:

$$\rho \frac{\partial \mathbf{v}}{\partial t} + \rho(\mathbf{v} \cdot \nabla)\mathbf{v} = -\nabla p + \eta \nabla^2 \mathbf{v} + \frac{\eta}{3} \nabla(\nabla \cdot \mathbf{v}) \qquad (6)$$

wherein $\mathbf{v}$ = velocity of fluid
                 ρ = its density
                 p = pressure
                 η = viscosity coefficient

It is useful to look at this equation, term by term, commencing at the left-hand side. The first term has the dimensions of a force per unit volume, as of course do all the others, and its meaning is obvious. Physically, the second term arises because a fluid, being mobile, may have a gradient of velocity with a component in the direction of the velocity, a characteristic which is impossible in a rigid body. The third term, being the gradient of a pressure, equals a force per unit volume. The fourth term represents the force which arises because of the shearing stress set up in a viscous fluid. The final term arises out of the shear stress set up when the volume element is distorted, i.e., when the fluid is compressible. If any external forces are present, these, of course, must be added, but for our purposes we have assumed that none exist.

Now the above equation may be written in an alternate form by making use of two well-known vector transformations, viz.,

$$(\mathbf{v} \cdot \nabla)\mathbf{v} = \tfrac{1}{2}\nabla v^2 - \mathbf{v} \times \nabla \times \mathbf{v}$$
$$\nabla \times \nabla \times \mathbf{v} = \nabla(\nabla \cdot \mathbf{v}) - \nabla^2 \mathbf{v}$$

The equation then reads

$$\rho \frac{\partial \mathbf{v}}{\partial t} + \rho\nabla \frac{v^2}{2} - \rho(\mathbf{v} \times \nabla \times \mathbf{v}) = -\nabla p + \frac{4\eta}{3} \nabla(\nabla \cdot \mathbf{v}) - \eta \nabla \times \nabla \times \mathbf{v}$$

$$(7)$$

For an incompressible liquid $(\nabla \cdot \mathbf{v} = 0)$ in irrotational motion $(\nabla \times \mathbf{v} = 0)$ in the steady state $(\partial \mathbf{v}/\partial t = 0)$ this reduces to Bernoulli's equation as, of course, it must.

In any particular problem, the solution of the differential equation must, as always, be fitted to the boundary conditions involved. Generally speaking, this equation is mathematically quite intractable, and a lot of the difficulty arises from the nonlinear term $\rho(\mathbf{v} \cdot \nabla)\mathbf{v}$. It is very common practice, therefore, to ignore this term, justifying this by the somewhat lame excuse that the velocities are to be small and hence squares are neglectable.

VISCOUS WAVES

Hydrodynamics is by the way of becoming a lost art, and the average present-day student of physics is but little acquainted with it because his instructors prefer to leave the matter to the airplane designers. It may be instructive, therefore, to consider an elementary problem involving the Navier-Stokes equation.

Consider a solid boundary (of infinite extent in the xy plane) immersed in an infinite ocean of viscous liquid. Permit this boundary to execute small-amplitude low-frequency simple harmonic motion in the x direction of angular frequency ω. The fluid in the immediate vicinity of the wall will, because of its viscosity, have a velocity which is the same as the boundary. Further, let the velocity be small and the liquid incompressible.   Then Eq. (6) becomes

$$\rho \frac{\partial \mathbf{v}}{\partial t} = \eta \nabla^2 \mathbf{v} - \nabla p \tag{8}$$

Under our assumed boundary conditions we must clearly have

$$\frac{\partial v}{\partial x} = 0 \qquad \frac{\partial v}{\partial y} = 0 \tag{9a}$$

$$z = \infty \qquad v = 0 \tag{9b}$$

$$z = 0 \qquad v = v_0 e^{i\omega t} \tag{9c}$$

Our condition (9c) is written in complex notation, and in the final solution we understand that we are to take the imaginary part of the expression.   Further, since the velocity is to be small everywhere, we neglect both the terms $(\mathbf{v} \cdot \nabla)\mathbf{v}$ and ∇p in the Navier-Stokes equation. The reason for neglecting the first of these is obvious, and ∇p, which is the Bernoulli pressure in this case, depends on the square of the fluid velocity and is therefore also negligible.

Hence Eq. (8) becomes

$$\frac{\partial v}{\partial t} = \frac{\eta}{\rho} \frac{\partial^2 v}{\partial z^2} \tag{10}$$

The quantity $\nu = \eta/\rho$, which is very common in fluid dynamics, is known as the "kinematic viscosity."

As is usual, assume

$$v = T(t)Z(z)$$

that is,

$$\frac{1}{T} \frac{dT}{dt} = \frac{\nu}{Z} \frac{d^2 Z}{dz^2} = \beta \ (\text{const})$$

The constant β may, of course, be positive, negative, or a complex number, whence

$$T = Ce^{\beta t} \tag{11a}$$

$$Z = F \exp\left(\sqrt{\frac{\beta}{\nu}} z\right) + G \exp\left(-\sqrt{\frac{\beta}{\nu}} z\right) \tag{11b}$$

Applying boundary condition (9c) to (11a), we see that $\beta = i\omega$, where ω is, of course, a real number.   Hence

$$v = Ce^{i\omega t}\left[F \exp\left(\sqrt{i} \sqrt{\frac{\omega}{\nu}} z\right) + G \exp\left(-\sqrt{i} \sqrt{\frac{\omega}{\nu}} z\right)\right]$$

Now $\qquad (1 + i)^2 = 2i \qquad$ or $\qquad \sqrt{i} = \dfrac{1 + i}{\sqrt{2}}$

and so

$$v = Ce^{i\omega t}\left[F \exp\left(i\sqrt{\frac{\omega}{2\nu}}\, z\right) \exp\left(\sqrt{\frac{\omega}{2\nu}}\, z\right) \right.$$
$$\left. + G \exp\left(-i\sqrt{\frac{\omega}{2\nu}}\, z\right) \exp\left(-\sqrt{\frac{\omega}{2\nu}}\, z\right) \right]$$

Applying boundary condition (9b) to the above, it is clear that $F = 0$. And so our final solution reads

$$v = v_0 \exp\left(-\sqrt{\frac{\omega}{2\nu}}\, z\right) \sin\left(\omega t - \sqrt{\frac{\omega}{2\nu}}\, z\right) \qquad (12)$$

This is a plane wave, traveling in the positive z direction, whose amplitude decreases exponentially from the source. The phase velocity $\sqrt{2\nu\omega}$ depends on the frequency, and hence the wave suffers dispersion.

As is customary in this kind of thing, we define "a penetration depth for viscous waves," δ such that

$$v_{z=\delta} = \frac{1}{e}\, v_{z=0}$$

whence, from (12),

$$\delta = \sqrt{\frac{2\nu}{\omega}} \qquad (13)[1]$$

In the case of He II, which has a very small kinematic viscosity, it is clear that the waves decay at distances very close to the oscillating source of the disturbance, and it is useful to make a numerical estimate. Thus, for He II

$$\nu \sim 10^{-4} \quad \text{cm}^2/\text{sec}$$

and taking $P = 30$ sec, we get that

$$\delta \sim 0.3 \text{ mm}$$

We have chosen the infinite wall, in the above analysis, since this is the easiest case to treat from the mathematical viewpoint. Had we chosen a pair of concentric circular discs, narrowly separated and oscillating about an axis perpendicular to their plane and through the center, the analysis would have been more complicated. Nevertheless, the physical principles are similar in the two cases. Since the superfluid possesses no viscosity, the penetration depth is here zero;

---

[1] In terms of the period of oscillation, P, this becomes $\delta = \sqrt{\nu P/\pi}$, a form sometimes used in the literature.

i.e., no viscous wave is produced.　If the disc separation is less than δ for the normal fluid, then the latter will possess nearly the same motion as the discs; i.e., it will be "trapped" between them.　This, as will emerge, forms the basis for the empirical determination of the ratio ρ_n/ρ.

ANDRONIKASHVILI'S EXPERIMENT

In our original postulates the ratio ρ_n/ρ was stated to be a temperature-dependent function with, however, only the end points

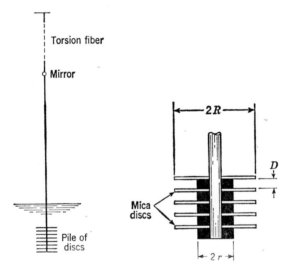

FIG. 25. Schematic of the arrangement used by Andronikashvili (1946) to determine ρ_n/ρ as a function of temperature.　Each disc was about 3 mils thick, approximately 1.5 in. diam and spaced about 10 mils apart.

specified.　It would clearly be of great interest to determine, experimentally, the explicit form of this function.　This was first done by Andronikashvili in 1946;[1] the method had been suggested earlier (1941) by Landau.　The experiment constitutes one of the most elegant ever undertaken in the field of low-temperature physics.　The apparatus (Fig. 25) consists of a series of thin discs narrowly separated from one another as shown.　The assembly is suspended, via a torsion fiber, from the top of the cryostat and provided with a small mirror so that torsional oscillations of the disc system can be observed.　Thus,

[1] E. Andronikashvili, *J. Phys. U.S.S.R.*, **10**:201 (1946).

in a vacuum, the period P_0 of the oscillations will be

$$P_0 = 2\pi \sqrt{\frac{I_0}{k}} \tag{14}$$

where I_0 = moment of inertia of disc system
k = torsion-fiber constant
This period is of the order of 30 sec, and the amplitude of the oscillation is kept small.

If now the disc system is immersed in He II, the period of oscillation will be found to have increased because the normal component, possessing viscosity, will follow the motion of the discs provided that the separation of the latter is small enough, i.e., of the order of the viscous penetration depth. The superfluid will, as usual, ignore the motion. Hence in He II the period will become

$$P = 2\pi \sqrt{\frac{I_0 + I_l}{k}} \tag{15}$$

where I_l is the moment of inertia of the liquid trapped between, and moving with, the discs. At about 1.7°K, for example, the penetration depth [formula (13)] is of the order of 0.5 mm. Andronikashvili used a spacing of approximately 0.2 mm in his system. Calling

$$\omega_0 = \frac{2\pi}{P_0} \qquad \omega = \frac{2\pi}{P} \qquad \tau = \frac{\omega_0}{\omega}$$

then
$$I_l = I_0(\tau^2 - 1) \tag{16}$$

Since the right-hand side of the above expression is known or measurable, it remains to relate I_l to ρ_n. This involves a rather more sophisticated solution of the Navier-Stokes equation than considered in our simple example. The result,[1] which was also stated without proof in Andronikashvili's paper, is

$$I_l = \frac{\pi}{2} \rho_n N (R^4 - r^4) 2D \left(1 + \frac{2\delta}{R}\right) + \frac{\pi}{2} \rho_n R^4 \delta$$
$$+ \pi \rho_n R^3 \, d\delta (N + 1) \tag{17}$$

$$\delta = \sqrt{\frac{2\eta}{\rho_n \omega}}$$

Here (see Fig. 25) R is the disc radius and r the spacer radius. D is the disc separation and d the thickness of each disc. The system consists of $(N + 1)$ equally spaced discs.

[1] A. C. Hollis-Hallett, *Proc. Roy. Soc. (London)*, **A210**:404 (1952).

Reading from left to right, the physical meanings of the three terms are as follows:

The first term is the moment of inertia of the liquid carried between the discs increased by the factor $(1 + 2\delta/R)$, which takes into account the liquid dragged by the edges of the laminae of liquid between the discs. The second term is the moment of inertia of liquid dragged by the exposed surfaces of the top and bottom discs. The third term is the moment of inertia of the liquid dragged by the edges of the discs.

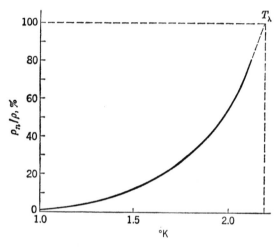

FIG. 26. The ratio ρ_n/ρ as a function of temperature. (*Andronikashvili*, 1946.) The experimental data fit well the relation $\rho_n/\rho = (T/T_\lambda)^{5.6}$.

Clearly, the first term is the most important one, since N is large ($\sim$100) and δ is small. Equally worthy of notice is the fact that, as Andronikashvili found, I_l decreases with decreasing temperature, which means that the density in question is that of the normal component, ρ_n, and not that of the full liquid, which is, as we know, substantially independent of temperature in He II. A plot of the result is shown in Fig. 26.

The Andronikashvili experiment has subsequently been studied in greater detail by Hollis-Hallett.[1] Among other things, he observed that the period of oscillation in He II was constant only below a certain critical amplitude of oscillation; above the latter the period was not a constant at all amplitudes. It appears, therefore, that above this critical amplitude the superfluid somehow loses its frictionless character and begins to be dragged with the normal component. The

[1] *Ibid.*

reasons for this are not, at the moment, well understood; it may be that some sort of turbulence (vortex motions) is induced in the previously stationary superfluid, which then interacts with the moving normal fluid.

VISCOSITY OF LIQUID HELIUM

As has been stated, three classical methods for measuring the viscosity of liquids have been used for liquid helium, viz., (1) Poiseuille flow, (2) oscillating disc, and (3) rotating cylinder. We have seen

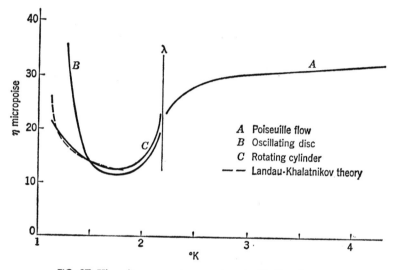

FIG. 27. Viscosity versus temperature in He I and He II.

that the first is not usable for He II, but can be and has been applied to He I. Method 2 suffers from the disadvantage that it measures the product of the density (of the normal component in He II) and the viscosity coefficient. In view of Andronikashvili's work, however, this is not a serious drawback. Method 3 is absolute and would appear well suited to the He II problem.

Figure 27 shows the results obtained with all three methods. Curve A, by Bowers and Mendelssohn,[1] was obtained by method 1. Curve B is a composite of concordant results by several investigators[2] using

[1] R. Bowers and K. Mendelssohn, *Proc. Roy. Soc. (London)*, **A204**:366 (1950).

[2] E. Andronikashvili, *J. Exptl. Theoret. Phys. (U.S.S.R.)*, **18**:429 (1948); A. C. Hollis-Hallett, *loc. cit.*; A. de Troyer, A. van Itterbeek, and G. van der Berg, *Physica*, **18**:50 (1951).

method 2, and curve C is due to Heikkila and Hollis-Hallett[1] using method 3. The dotted curve in Fig. 27 is a theoretical calculation by Landau and Khalatnikov,[2] valid below about 1.8°K, using Landau's theory of He II, which will be discussed later.

The results of methods 2 and 3 are in fair agreement, except at the lowest temperatures. This may very likely be accounted for by the fact that the oscillating-disc method, depending as it does on a knowledge of ρ_n, is inherently less accurate than the rotating-cylinder method.[3] There is, however, a somewhat disturbing element involved in both methods, as was first shown by Hollis-Hallett.

This arises from the fact that the viscosity is independent of the peripheral velocity of the outer cylinder only up to a small velocity of the order of 0.1 cm/sec. Above this value the measured viscosity appears to increase steadily. At first this was thought to be an effect peculiar to He II; however, Hollis-Hallett[4] has now demonstrated its existence in a purely classical liquid (carbon disulfide), albeit in the latter liquid the "critical velocity" involved is much higher than for He II. It would seem, therefore, that the effect is due to hydrodynamic turbulence generated in the helium once a certain flow velocity is exceeded. It must be admitted, though, that this explanation is somewhat unsatisfying since we have only the haziest notion, at the moment, as to what constitutes turbulence in the superfluid component of He II.

[1] W. J. Heikkila and A. C. Hollis-Hallett, *Can. J. Phys.*, **33**:420 (1955).

[2] L. Landau and I. Khalatnikov, *J. Exptl. Theoret. Phys. (U.S.S.R.)*, **19**:637 (1949).

[3] It is also, at the lower temperatures, less accurate for other reasons; see reference 1, p. 49.

[4] Fifth International Conference on Low Temperature Physics and Chemistry, Madison, Wisconsin, 1957.

CHAPTER 4

Entropy Waves
or Second Sound

SOME CONSERVATION THEOREMS

For future reference, it is necessary to state, and occasionally prove, some propositions in which such quantities as mass and entropy are conserved. Consider first the hydrodynamical current density

$$\mathbf{j} = \rho\mathbf{v}$$

This has the cgs dimensions of g/cm^2 sec; i.e., it is the mass transported across unit area per second by a current whose velocity is $\mathbf{v}$ and density ρ.

Clearly,

$$\frac{\partial\rho}{\partial t} + \nabla\cdot\mathbf{j} = 0 \tag{1}$$

This states that the net mass flow into a small element of volume must equal the time rate of change of mass in the volume. If the fluid is incompressible, then $\partial\rho/\partial t = 0$ and, from (1), $\nabla\cdot\mathbf{v} = 0$.

Again, if there is a gradient of pressure in a liquid, there will be a net force on a small-volume element which, by Newton's second law, equals the time rate of change of momentum, i.e.,

$$\frac{\partial(\rho\mathbf{v})}{\partial t} + \nabla p = 0$$

or

$$\frac{\partial\mathbf{j}}{\partial t} + \nabla p = 0 \tag{2}$$

Elimination of $\mathbf{j}$ between Eqs. (1) and (2) leads, as is well known, to an equation showing that the pressure is propagated as a wave, i.e., ordinary sound.　Clearly, both these equations apply equally well to either the normal or superfluid components of He II, and hence sound is transmitted in this fluid as in any other.　The measured value of the velocity is of the order of some 240 m/sec.

The normal component of the He II, according to our postulates, possesses all the heat energy (and hence entropy) of the fluid.　Hence if a point in He II is held at an elevated temperature, superfluid will stream toward this place and a balancing flow of normal component, carrying heat with it, will move away.　And if we consider He II to be incompressible, which is very nearly so, then

$$\rho_n \mathbf{v}_n + \rho_s \mathbf{v}_s = 0 \tag{3}$$

The subscripts n and s refer to normal and superfluid components, respectively, and Eq. (3) defines two velocity fields.

Consider next 1 g of He II, of which a fraction x is in the normal state and the remainder $(1 - x)$ is superfluid.　Clearly, $x = \rho_n/\rho$.　If we call the entropy (per gram) of normal fluid S_n and consider a stream flowing with velocity v_n, then in 1 sec the total entropy flowing across unit area must be

$$x\rho S_n v_n \qquad \text{cal/}^\circ\text{K cm}^2 \text{ sec}$$

And if the entropy (per gram) of He II is S, then

$$S = x S_n + (1 - x)0 = x S_n$$

i.e., the entropy stream is

$$\rho S v_n \tag{4}$$

If we consider the flow to possess no irreversibilities and hence are able to apply the second law, then the heat current will be

$$\dot{q} = \rho S T v_n \qquad \text{cal/cm}^2 \text{ sec} \tag{5}$$

Equations (3) to (5) represent a powerful and unique mechanism for transferring heat, a great deal more potent than the classical process of heat conduction by diffusion.　And although the process was styled "internal convection" by F. London, it is quite distinct from the ordinary convection process in a gas or liquid, which depends on the buoyant force produced by density variation with temperature.

We may readily compute the size of the velocity of the normal component in He II via Eq. (5).　Thus at 1.5°K, $S \cong 0.2$ joules/g °K, and for a power input of 100 milliwatts/cm^2 we find that $v_n \cong 2.3$ cm/sec.

Since in most experiments the heat input is usually less than this, we see that, generally speaking, v_n is a small quantity. Knowing v_n we can, of course, find the corresponding value of v_s from Eq. (3).

The above considerations allow us to write down yet another conservation equation. Consider a point (x,y,z) in a batch of He II at which the normal-component velocity is

$$\mathbf{v}_n = \mathbf{v}_x + \mathbf{v}_y + \mathbf{v}_z$$

In the usual way, construct an elemental cube of dimensions $dx\,dy\,dz$ with this point at its center. In the x direction the entropy carried into the volume will be

$$\left[\rho S v_x - \frac{\partial}{\partial x}\,(\rho S v_x)\,\frac{dx}{2} \right] dy\,dz \qquad \text{cal/°K sec}$$

and the entropy leaving the cube at the opposite face is

$$\left[\rho S v_x + \frac{\partial}{\partial x}\,(\rho S v_x)\,\frac{dx}{2} \right] dy\,dz$$

Considering also the other two directions in space, we then have that the net decrease in entropy in the cube per second is

$$\left[\frac{\partial}{\partial x}\,(\rho S v_x) + \frac{\partial}{\partial y}\,(\rho S v_y) + \frac{\partial}{\partial y}\,(\rho S v_z) \right] dx\,dy\,dz$$

if, and only if, there are no sources or sinks of heat within the cube or otherwise thermodynamically irreversible processes occurring within it. Under these conditions, then, the above must equal

$$-\frac{\partial}{\partial t}\,(\rho S)\,dx\,dy\,dz \qquad \text{cal/°K sec}$$

i.e., finally,

$$\frac{\partial}{\partial t}\,(\rho S) + \nabla \cdot (\rho S \mathbf{v}_n) = 0 \qquad (6)$$

And for our situation where ρ is assumed constant, this simplifies to

$$\frac{\partial S}{\partial t} + \nabla \cdot (S \mathbf{v}_n) = 0 \qquad (7)$$

THERMAL CONDUCTION IN He II

In the late thirties, before the two-fluid nature of He II was widely recognized, a number of attempts to measure the thermal conductivity of He II were made.   Classically speaking, the conduction of heat is governed by the following relation:

$$\frac{\partial T}{\partial t} = \frac{K}{\rho C} \nabla^2 T \tag{8}$$

where K = coefficient of thermal conductivity
ρ = density of medium
C = its specific heat
In the case of steady-state conduction in one dimension (i.e., along a wire) one solution of the above gives a linear temperature gradient. This is the basis of the method used to measure K, since in this case

$$\dot{H} = K\nabla T \tag{9}$$

where $\dot{H}$ has the cgs units of cal/cm² sec.
   A "wire" of liquid is conveniently produced by enclosing it in a not-too-narrow capillary, one end of which is in contact with the bath; the other is electrically heated.   Resistance thermometers are employed to measure temperature gradients.   The results show that He II, unlike He I, fails to obey Eq. (8); in other words, $\dot{H}$ is not a linear function of grad T but much more complicated.   If one tries to "force" the helium to obey the classical relation (9) by taking the slope of the $\dot{H}$ versus grad T curve, quite extraordinary thermal conductivities result, sometimes of the order of 800 times that of copper at room temperature.   The effective thermal conductivity of He II is indeed astonishingly large, but this is entirely due, as we have seen, to the unique mechanism of internal convection.   If this process is suppressed by going to temperatures much below 1°K, then He II reverts to a liquid with an ordinary heat conduction obeying Eq. (8) in which the thermal conductivity is tiny.

THE SECOND SOUND

   Tisza in 1940 and, apparently quite independently, Landau in 1941 developed theories of He II.   The two theories were totally different in concept, but each arrived at a set of conditions not too different from those which we have labeled as postulates in Chap. 3. On the basis of these, both deduced that small fluctuations in entropy (or temperature, which amounts to the same thing) are propagated as an undamped dispersionless wave in He II.   It is only fair to say, however, that Landau's theory has stood the test of time much better than Tisza's and contains many of the elements which an ultimate theory must also possess.   In deducing the wave equation, we shall make use of a simplified analysis employed later on by Gogate and Pathak.[1] This has the advantage of making the physical picture rather clearer; it suffers the disadvantage of failing to reveal certain points which Landau's more sophisticated analysis[2] brings to light.

Imagine an electric heater, fed with a small alternating current, immersed in a batch of He II (Fig. 28). Consider two parallel planes, each 1 cm² in area, a distance dx apart; the temperature at one call T and at the other $(T + \Delta T)$. Our electric heater (as is the case in the majority of the experiments to be presently described) will be a plane source of heat fed with a few milliwatts of power (frequency ω) so that it creates *small* fluctuations in temperature (and entropy) and, as we

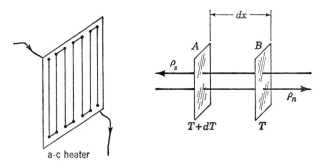

FIG. 28. Two unit area planes a distance dx apart at right angles to a heat current in He II.

have seen, gives rise to small normal-component velocities. If the resistance of the element at the ambient temperature T_0 is R, then the heat input $\dot{q}$ will be

$$\dot{q} \propto R(i_0 \sin \omega t)^2$$
$$\propto \frac{i_0{}^2 R}{2} (1 - \cos 2\omega t)$$

This means that the source will fluctuate at twice the frequency of the electric current and, in addition, will put out a steady heat flow which is, however, irrelevant to our discussion. The situation, as far as the temperature or entropy fluctuations are concerned, is illustrated in Fig. 29.

The entropy and temperature may be divided into two terms as follows:

$$S = S_0 + S^*$$
$$T = T_0 + T^* \tag{10}$$

[1] D. Gogate and P. Pathak, *Proc. Phys. Soc. (London)*, **59**:457 (1947).
[2] L. Landau, *J. Phys. (U.S.S.R.)*, **5**:71 (1941).

S_0 and T_0 are the ambient entropy and temperature, and the starred values are small departures therefrom. For example, T_0 might be 1.5°K, whereas T^* would be of the order of a few millidegrees. Clearly, the ambient values are constants, whereas the starred values are certainly functions of time and, owing to the inertia of the fluids,

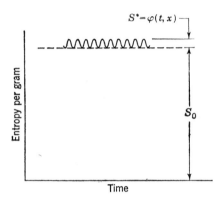

FIG. 29. Small entropy fluctuations superimposed on a large steady ambient value.

almost equally certainly functions of position x. Thus for our case, Eq. (7) reads

$$\frac{\partial S^*}{\partial t} + \frac{\partial}{\partial x}(S_0 + S^*)v_n = 0$$

that is, $$\frac{\partial S^*}{\partial t} + S_0 \frac{\partial v_n}{\partial x} + S^* \frac{\partial v_n}{\partial x} + v_n \frac{\partial S^*}{\partial x} = 0$$

Since S^* and v_n are both very small, we may, as a first approximation, ignore the last two terms and get

$$\frac{\partial S^*}{\partial t} + S_0 \frac{\partial v_n}{\partial x} = 0 \tag{11}$$

Now entropy in the amount $\rho S_0 v_n$ [cf. Eq. (4)] is carried from one plane in Fig. 28 to the other. If, as we are supposing, this flow process is reversible, then an amount of work $\rho S_0 v_n \, dT$ must be done on the liquid. Alternatively, this is the excess of heat flowing in over that flowing out of the element of volume dx in one second.[1] This energy flow must appear as an increase in the kinetic energy of the two streams in the volume.

[1] Since the normal fluid possesses viscosity, the assumed reversibility of the process is obviously questionable. However, the viscosity is small (cf. Chap. 3), so we ignore it.

Now the kinetic energy density of the two streams is clearly

$$\tfrac{1}{2}(\rho_n v_n{}^2 + \rho_s v_s{}^2) \qquad \text{ergs/cm}^3$$

and eliminating v_s via Eq. (3) plus the fact that $\rho = \rho_n + \rho_s$, we get

$$\frac{\rho \rho_n}{2\rho_s} v_n{}^2 \tag{12}[1]$$

Thus we have

$$\rho S_0 v_n \, dT = \frac{\partial}{\partial t}\left(\frac{\rho \rho_n}{2\rho_s} v_n{}^2\right) dx$$

that is,

$$S_0 \, dT = \frac{\rho_n}{\rho_s} v_n \, dx \tag{13}$$

since ρ_n and ρ_s are largely the ambient values corresponding to T_0 and are thus independent of time.[2]

Differentiating Eq. (11) with respect to time, we then get

$$\frac{\partial^2 S^*}{\partial t^2} = -S_0 \frac{\partial^2 v_n}{\partial x \, \partial t} = -S_0 \frac{\partial \dot v_n}{\partial x} \tag{14}$$

Similarly, from (13),

$$S_0 \frac{\partial^2 T}{\partial x^2} = -\frac{\rho_n}{\rho_s} \frac{\partial \dot v_n}{\partial x} \tag{15}$$

whence, combining (14) and (15), we get

$$\frac{\partial^2 S^*}{\partial t^2} = S_0{}^2 \frac{\rho_s}{\rho_n} \frac{\partial^2 T^*}{\partial x^2} \tag{16}$$

Now

$$T_0 \, dS^* = dU + p \, dV = C_0 \, dT^* + p \, dV \tag{17}$$

where C_0 is the ambient specific heat; since changes in the volume will be small (owing to the small temperature fluctuations plus the fact that the coefficient of thermal expansion of He II is also small), we may

---

[1] The following is an identity:

$$\tfrac{1}{2}(\rho_n v_n{}^2 + \rho_s v_s{}^2) = \frac{1}{2\rho}(\rho_n v_n + \rho_s v_s)^2 + \frac{\rho_s \rho_n}{2\rho}(v_s - v_n)^2$$

and is quoted by some authors. It clearly leads to the same result as (12).

[2] Equation (13) can be generalized to read

$$\rho_n \dot v_n = -\rho_s S_0 \, \text{grad } T$$

The minus sign appears since T is decreasing as x is increasing (Fig. 28). The right-hand side of this equation is the fountain-pressure gradient in the super-fluid and turns out to be equal and opposite to the force per unit volume on the normal fluid. Accordingly, it represents the Newtonian third law for the interaction between the two fluids.

neglect the last term on the right of (17). Equation (16) will then read

$$\frac{\partial^2 S^*}{\partial t^2} = \frac{T_0 S_0{}^2 \rho_s}{C_0 \rho_n} \frac{\partial^2 S^*}{\partial x^2}$$

or

$$\frac{\partial^2 T^*}{\partial t^2} = \frac{T_0 S_0{}^2 \rho_s}{C_0 \rho_n} \frac{\partial^2 T^*}{\partial x^2} \tag{18}$$

This is the equation of an undamped wave propagated with a velocity u_2 given by

$$u_2{}^2 = \frac{\rho_s}{\rho_n} \frac{T_0 S_0{}^2}{C_0} \tag{19}$$

Substituting experimentally known values of the various quantities into Eq. (19) at, say, 1.5°K leads to a value of u_2 of around 20 m/sec. Clearly, also, the velocity vanishes at the λ point since here ρ_s becomes zero. Thus both in temperature dependence and absolute magnitude the velocity of these "entropy waves" is very different from ordinary sound.[1]

Landau, in his original paper, operated from a rather more general point of view. He added to our Eqs. (1), (2), and (6) one reading

$$\frac{\partial v_s}{\partial t} + \nabla \varphi = 0$$

Here φ is the Gibbs free energy $(h - TS)$ of the He II; a constant φ will lead to H. London's fountain-pressure formula. The same assumptions as to the smallness of the entropy fluctuations are, of course, made. This formulation, to quote his words, leads to the

---

[1] Alternatively, we can proceed as follows:

$$\rho_n \dot{v}_n = -\rho_s S_0 \frac{\partial T^*}{\partial x}$$

$$\frac{\partial S^*}{\partial t} = -S_0 \frac{\partial v_n}{\partial x}$$

$$T_0 \, dS^* = C_0 \, dT^*$$

Thus

$$\rho_n \ddot{v}_n = -\rho_s S_0 \frac{\partial^2 T^*}{\partial x \, \partial t} = -\frac{\rho_s S_0 T_0}{C_0} \frac{\partial^2 S^*}{\partial x \, \partial t}$$

that is,

$$\ddot{v}_n = \frac{\rho_s}{\rho_n} \frac{S_0{}^2 T_0}{C_0} \frac{\partial^2 v_n}{\partial x^2}$$

and since $v_s = -\rho_n v_n / \rho_s$ [cf. Eq. (3)],

$$\ddot{v}_s = \frac{\rho_s}{\rho_n} \frac{S_0{}^2 T_0}{C_0} \frac{\partial^2 v_s}{\partial x^2}$$

Thus both velocities propagate as a wave but are opposite in phase.

result "that there must be two velocities of sound in helium II." This is unfortunately somewhat misleading and subsequently caused some trouble for the experimentalists. Actually Landau's analysis shows that both pressure waves (ordinary sound) and the above entropy waves are propagated in He II. Further, there is a weak coupling between the two types of vibration. Thus he called the temperature wave "second sound" as distinct from the pressure wave ("first sound"). This terminology is now universally employed.

EXPERIMENTAL VERIFICATION

Resonance Methods. The first experimental verification of the preceding discussion was obtained by Peshkov as early as 1944, and two years later he published a full account of his work,[1] wherein the second sound velocity was measured from about 1.1°K to the λ point.

Based on Landau's work, Shalnikov and Sokolov had attempted to detect second sound about 1941. Their efforts met with no success because they tried to generate the entropy wave by means of a piezo-electric crystal immersed in the liquid. It would appear that the term "second sound" was being taken a little too literally. It remained for Lifshitz to show[2] that a piezo transducer radiates second sound with about a millionth the intensity of ordinary sound, whereas in a fluctuating temperature source the second sound is some five thousand times more intense than the first sound.[3] Once this much was clear, success was assured.

Since the temperature pulses were to be small, Peshkov adopted a resonance method to amplify the effect, and a schematic of his experimental arrangement is shown in Fig. 30. The heater consisted of a plane source made by winding 20-μ-diam constantan wire in the form of a bifilar spiral on a flat ivory disc. In contrast to pure metals, the alloy constantan has a resistance at helium temperatures which is close to the room-temperature value. The thermometers, of which there were two, were made of 30-μ phosphor bronze wire, also wound in a spiral somewhat like a spider web.

The three elements were mounted in a vertical glass tube, which we will call a cavity. One thermometer was fixed at the bottom of the cavity; the other and the heater were separately movable (from outside

[1] V. Peshkov, *J. Phys.* (*U.S.S.R.*), **8**:381 (1944); **10**:389 (1946).

[2] E. Lifshitz, *J. Phys.* (*U.S.S.R.*), **8**:110 (1944).

[3] A fluctuating heat source, owing to the slight change in density of the liquid on heating, will radiate pressure waves. This is the basis of the "thermophone" used in acoustics.

the cryostat) accurately known distances along the axis.   The heater was fed with sinusoidal alternating current of fixed frequency producing, as we have seen, entropy and temperature fluctuations of double this frequency.   The thermometers were fed a small d-c current; accordingly, temperature fluctuations produced corresponding changes in resistance of the thermometer which, because of the d-c current through it, showed up as a voltage fluctuation across the instrument.

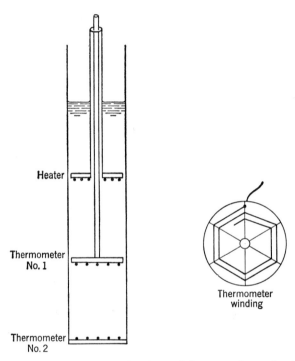

FIG. 30. Schematic of arrangement for determining second sound velocity using standing waves.   (*Peshkov*, 1946.)

This signal was amplified by a conventional vacuum-tube amplifier and presented on one pair of plates of an oscilloscope.   The other pair were fed by the heater current frequency.   Thus the second sound, on this display scheme, showed up as a Lissajous figure corresponding to the frequency doubling on one pair of plates and thus was distinguishable from ordinary electromagnetic pickup, which would have the same frequency as the source.

The second sound wave, when reflected from the bottom of the cavity, produced a standing-wave pattern (similar to an organ pipe in acoustics); by tuning the cavity by varying the distance of the heater from the bottom, resonance could be achieved, i.e., when an integral number of half-wavelengths just fitted into the cavity. Under this condition, it turned out that the bottom of the cavity (as read on the thermometer there) became a temperature antinode along with the heater surface. The wavelength determination consisted in moving the second thermometer from one signal maximum to the next; this distance, of course, was half a wavelength. Since the frequency was known, this then yielded the velocity.

Peshkov reported the resonances at various temperatures to be very sharp, thus indicating a high Q for the cavity, in other words, very little energy loss or attenuation of the wave. Also an attempt was made to detect a dispersion at the temperature of maximum velocity (1.63°K) by measuring the velocity for a range of frequencies between 100 and 10,000 cycles. The velocity (20.36 m/sec) was found independent of frequency to within 0.1 per cent. Using Andronikashvili's values for the normal-component density, Peshkov found his results in excellent agreement with Landau's formula [our Eq. (19)].

Historically, the second measurement of the velocity was carried out in 1946 by Lane, Fairbank, and Fairbank,[1,2] who were aware of Peshkov's 1944 result but not of his work published in 1946. Hence some duplication occurred. These authors also employed a resonance technique and used a heater to generate the second sound, but they had some interesting variations of Peshkov's method. Figure 31 shows the cavity employed in this experiment. The plane source heater is at the bottom, and a small magnetic microphone is attached to the top end. The cavity is partially filled with liquid helium, from the surrounding bath, via small holes. Resonant conditions occur when the depth of liquid in the cavity equals an integral number of half-wavelengths. Provided the free surface of the liquid is a temperature antinode at resonance, the temperature at this surface will fluctuate at double the frequency of the input alternating current. This will cause the liquid to evaporate in bursts, i.e., will produce density fluctuations (first sound) in the vapor, and the microphone will respond to these.

The microphone output was amplified conventionally, rectified, and displayed on a recording potentiometer; the paper moved at a constant rate. As the bath and the liquid in the attached cavity slowly evaporated, the recorder printed a series of resonance peaks (Fig. 32). The height of liquid in the cavity was measured as a function of time by

[1] C. Lane, H. Fairbank, H. Schultz, and W. Fairbank, *Phys. Rev.*, **70**:431 (1946).
[2] C. Lane, H. Fairbank, and W. Fairbank, *Phys. Rev.*, **71**:600 (1947).

means of a cathetometer and clock; the latter was synchronized with the recorder chart drive. This was accurately linear with time, as is usually the case for evaporation from a helium bath held at a fixed temperature. Since many resonance peaks were recorded in a single run, the method proved itself highly accurate for wavelength, and hence velocity, determinations; and the results proved to be in excellent agreement with Peshkov's values.

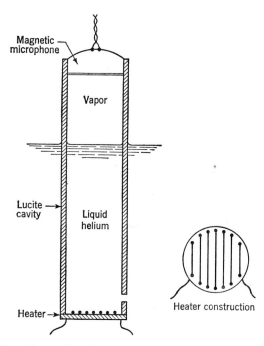

FIG. 31. Second sound cavity. (*Lane, Fairbank, and Fairbank, 1947.*)

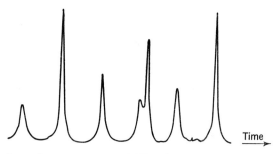

FIG. 32. Second sound resonances at 1.57°K registered on recorder from microphone in vapor above He II surface. (*Lane, Fairbank, and Fairbank, 1947.*)

The data showed that, at resonance, both the heater and free surface were antinodes and the Q values of the cavity were large, indicating small dissipation in the liquid or through the liquid surface. It will be observed that the resonances in Fig. 32 appear to be modulated by a much longer wavelength. This turns out to be a resonance effect of the first sound in the vapor portion of the cavity.

Somewhat later, the above authors tried the inverse of this method. The heater was replaced by a resistance thermometer and the microphone fed with an alternating current and used as a transducer. The resulting first sound in the vapor produced second sound in the liquid, resonances for which were observed on the thermometer.

Time-of-flight Method. An obvious way to determine velocity would be to time the flight of a temperature pulse over a known distance. Thus a path length of 10 cm is quite possible in a given cryostat and at 20 m/sec a short pulse would require 5 msec to negotiate it. Times of this size can be measured with great accuracy using known electronic techniques. Pellam[1] and Osborne,[2] working independently and at about the same time, were the first to use this method. And it has been employed by numerous workers since that time.

The heater, consisting either of a fine wire grid or a flat carbon strip, is fed single "rectangular" pulses of current. Typically the current rises to its full value in a time less than 1 μsec, remains constant for 100 to 200 μsec, and decays again to zero in a fraction of a microsecond. Such a pulse consists, of course, of a spectrum of frequencies; the important Fourier components of, say, a 150-μsec pulse are in the neighborhood of 3 kc. The method would seem to provide a good test for any possible dispersion of the second sound, since the latter would give rise to a distortion of the pulse shape. The detector is located a known distance away from the heater and consists, as usual, of a resistance thermometer.

There arises a difficulty, however, with the shape of the heat pulse obtained in the liquid, which is found to be no longer rectangular. The problem here is analogous to "mismatch" on an electric transmission line (in this case between the solid heater and the liquid helium) and is connected with a phenomenon known as the "Kapitza jump." Kapitza found that when heat flows from a solid surface into He II, there is a temperature discontinuity at or near the solid boundary proportional to the heat flow per unit area. This results in a rounding-off of the sharp edges of the electric pulse (it becomes more like a Gaussian curve). This pulse does not, however, suffer noticeable further distortion on its passage through the liquid.

[1] J. R. Pellam, *Phys. Rev.*, **74**:841 (1948).
[2] D. V. Osborne, *Nature*, **162**:213 (1948).

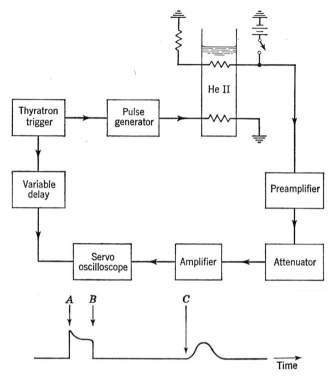

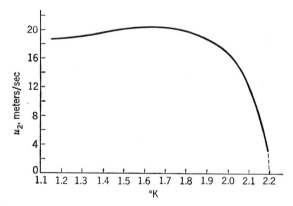

FIG. 33. Block diagram of electronics used in time-of-flight velocity determination, plus typical scope trace.   The transmitted pulse, beginning at A and ending at B, is picked up in the receiver by stray electromagnetic coupling.   Beginning of received pulse at C.   Time of flight $(A \rightarrow C)$ is accurately determined by superimposing on scope photograph signal from 50-kc sine-wave oscillator (not shown).

FIG. 34. Second sound velocity versus temperature.

A simplified block diagram of the electronics employed in this kind of work is shown in Fig. 33, which also shows a typical oscilloscope trace. The method leads, in general, to an accuracy comparable to the continuous-wave resonance techniques; in fact, the velocity determinations of different workers differ from one another so little that any one may be chosen as the definitive result. Figure 34 shows the velocity versus temperature curve; the data being that of Peshkov.

Above 1°K the second sound velocity has shown itself to be extraordinarily stable. Thus Wheeler, Blakewood, and Lane[1] have shown that the velocity does not change by as much as 0.1 per cent when the liquid is placed in a highly turbulent state induced by rapid stirring.

SECOND-ORDER EFFECTS

In our analysis of thermal waves second-order effects were generally ignored. Thus irreversibilities due to the finite viscosity of the normal component were disregarded, and we postulated that entropy fluctuations and the resulting fluid velocities should be held small. The above experiments generally obeyed the latter restriction; power inputs were around 0.1 watt/cm², often much less. The question thus arises as to what happens, experimentally, when the above restrictions are removed.

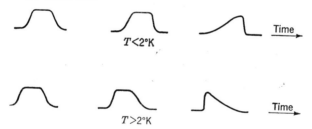

FIG. 35. Second sound pulse of large amplitude, at three successive positions in its path, showing "shock wave" effects. (*Osborne*, 1951.)

Osborne,[2] using the time-of-flight pulse method, found that whereas small pulses were propagated without noticeable change in shape, larger (i.e., greater amplitude) ones became seriously distorted. Further, the distortion of the pulse as it proceeded in its flight differed, depending on whether the measurement was made above about 2°K or below this temperature. The effect is sketched in Fig. 35, which is reproduced from a review article by Atkins (*Philosophical Magazine Supplement*, 1952).

[1] R. Wheeler, C. Blakewood, and C. Lane, *Phys. Rev.*, **99**:1667 (1955).
[2] D. V. Osborne, *Proc. Phys Soc. (London)*, **64**:114 (1951).

To those familiar with shock waves produced in air or water by intense explosions the above will appear reminiscent. And it is, in fact, due to the same cause, i.e., nonlinearities in the equation of motion. A theoretical treatment, due to Temperly,[1] shows that the top of the pulse travels with a velocity

$$u_{\text{top}} = u_2 + v_s + v_n$$

Here v_n will be in the same direction as u_2 and therefore positive; v_s will be in the opposite direction, since $\rho_n v_n + \rho_s v_s = 0$ and hence is negative. Below about 2°K, v_n is larger than v_s; above, smaller. Hence below 2°K the top of the pulse will travel faster than the bottom. The result of this is that the leading edge becomes steeper while the tail lengthens. Eventually a steep "shock front" is formed which travels with a velocity $u_2 + \frac{1}{2}(v_s + v_n)$.

ATTENUATION

In our previous discussion we ignored all irreversible effects occurring in the normal component and, as a result, deduced that the temperature waves should be undamped or, in other words, experience no attenuation in their passage through the liquid. Although the early experiments showed this to be a pretty fair approximation, later measurements have shown that there is a finite attenuation, albeit a small one.

Since we are trying to measure a small effect, any accuracy in the experiment presents great difficulties. At first sight it might seem that the best approach would be to use a pulse technique and measure the magnitude of the pulse height by means of two thermometers placed a known distance apart in the liquid. Since the attenuation is due to dissipative processes in the liquid, we might expect the pulse height H to be represented by

$$H = H_0 e^{-\alpha x}$$

where α is the desired attenuation coefficient.

This method has indeed been tried, but it involves some troubles. First, we must be very sure that the wave is plane; if it is not, the amplitude of the pulse will decrease with distance merely because the energy density of the wave is decreasing owing to the divergence of the beam ("beam spreading"). More disadvantageous is the fact that the pulse does not consist of a single frequency, but rather a spectrum thereof, and it turns out from theoretical considerations[2] that the attenuation constant α depends on the square of the frequency.

[1] H. N. V. Temperly, *Proc. Phys. Soc. (London)*, **A64**:105 (1951).

[2] I. M. Khalatnikov, *J. Exptl. Theoret. Phys. (U.S.S.R.)*, **23**:34 (1952).

Largely for the last reason, the most definitive work on attenuation, that of Hanson and Pellam,[1] makes use of a continuous-wave technique with a free traveling-wave system. Apart from the beam-spreading difficulty, which also applies to this method, it suffers uniquely from electromagnetic coupling ("crosstalk") between transmitter and receiver. This last is of no importance in the pulse method since here the second sound pulse and the crosstalk are separated in time and hence distinguishable, while in the continuous-wave technique they are not.

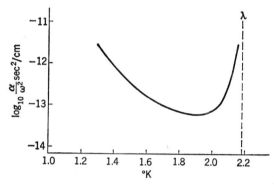

FIG. 36. Attenuation of second sound as a function of temperature for frequencies ranging from 100 to 268 kc. (*Hanson and Pellam,* 1954.)

Hanson and Pellam overcame these various difficulties first by operating in the 100-kc frequency range, thus assuring plane waves. Second, they overcame the crosstalk difficulty by noting that the received signal varied between a maximum and a minimum corresponding to the second sound and crosstalk being in phase or out of phase with each other. Averaging between the two thus eliminated the crosstalk. Observations on this averaged signal as a function of distance then gave the required attenuation constant. For a given temperature this was proportional to the square of the frequency ω, as the theory requires. Figure 36 shows their result, wherein α/ω^2 is plotted against temperature. The measurements are in excellent accord with Khalatnikov's views that the attenuation of second sound is caused by the viscosity of the normal component plus the irreversible effect of (classical) thermal conduction in the normal component.

RADIOMETER EFFECT AND RAYLEIGH DISC

As we have seen, a heat current in He II produces two flow velocities v_n and v_s related to each other via the internal-convection

[1] W. B. Hanson and J. R. Pellam, *Phys. Rev.*, **95**:321 (1954).

hypothesis, and each of these streams carries momentum. Accordingly, the "momentum current" $\langle P \rangle$ is given by

$$\langle P \rangle = \rho_n \mathbf{v}_n \cdot \mathbf{v}_n + \rho_s \mathbf{v}_s \cdot \mathbf{v}_s \qquad (20)$$

where $\langle P \rangle$ has the cgs dimensions of dynes per square centimeter or momentum per second per square centimeter.

If a plane material boundary, across which heat is made to flow, is immersed in a bath of He II held at a fixed ambient temperature T_0, this will experience a reaction force per square centimeter, f, given by Eq. (20), i.e.,

$$f = \rho_n v_n{}^2 + \rho_s v_s{}^2 \qquad (21)$$

But $\rho_n v_n + \rho_s v_s = 0$, and using this to eliminate v_s in (21) gives

$$f = \frac{\rho \rho_n}{\rho_s} v_n{}^2 \qquad (22)$$

Remembering that the heat flow $\dot{Q}$ across the boundary is carried away by the normal component, we have

$$\dot{Q} = \rho S_0 T_0 v_n$$

Using this to eliminate v_n in (22), we thus get

$$f = \frac{\rho_n}{\rho \rho_s} \left(\frac{\dot{Q}}{T_0 S_0} \right)^2 \qquad (23)$$

Thus if a small insulated vessel containing a source of heat and a plane heat conducting boundary is immersed in He II, it should experience a reaction pressure given by the above formula and thus provide a rather nice test of the soundness of our fundamental hypotheses.

Actually such an experiment was tried by Strelkov in 1940[1] and a repulsive force found. However, this was before the days of the two-fluid hypothesis, and formula (23) was unknown at the time. More recently Hall[2] has reexamined the matter, and his results are in substantial agreement with the above equation.

A not entirely dissimilar test of the two-fluid hypothesis has been made by Pellam and coworkers using the "Rayleigh disc."[3,4] If a small thin disc (radius a) is placed with its plane at an angle φ in a stream of fluid (density ρ) moving with velocity v, it will, as a consequence of Bernoulli effect, experience a torque τ tending to set it

[1] P. G. Strelkov, *J. Phys. (U.S.S.R.)*, **3**:53 (1940).

[2] H. E. Hall, *Proc. Phys. Soc. (London)*, **A67**:485 (1954).

[3] J. R. Pellam and P. Morse, *Phys. Rev.*, **78**:474 (1950).

[4] J. R. Pellam, "Progress in Low Temperature Physics," vol. I, Interscience Publishers, Inc., 1955.

crosswise to the flow and given by

$$\tau = \tfrac{4}{3}\rho a^3 v^2 \sin 2\varphi$$

The device was employed by Lord Rayleigh around 1880 to determine particle velocities and hence intensities in a sound field.

Pellam and Morse used this technique in a second sound field produced in a resonant cavity, with the disc suspended at an antinode of the heat current density. The result showed that both fluids contributed to the torque on the disc; the factor $(\dot{Q}/T_0 S_0)^2$ also appeared in this case.

OTHER METHODS OF GENERATION

The above work has, in every case, made use of an electric heater to produce the entropy fluctuations, a method which in itself is irreversible. Peshkov, in a later investigation,[1] has generated the second sound by means of an "entropy filter." This consisted of a cylindrical cavity one end of which was formed by a flexible metal diaphragm and the other by a porous copper filter. The diaphragm was oscillated by an arrangement similar to a radio loudspeaker; this caused a periodic flow of superfluid through the filter, whose pores were too fine to pass normal component. In other words, entropy fluctuations were created outside the cavity (cf. the mechano-caloric effect, Chap. 2).

The waves were detected, as usual, by a resistance thermometer, and their velocity was found to be in accord with the previous work. Clearly, for this method, the frequency of the second sound is the same as that of the pressure fluctuations (first sound). The amplitude of the latter was, however, smaller by about a factor of 6 (at 1.63°K) when the second sound was at resonance, and thus it was possible to distinguish which of the two waves were at resonance.

An interesting type of second sound generator, devised and used by Kurti and McIntosh,[2] makes use of a paramagnetic salt in an alternating magnetic field.[3] This technique removes the steady heat current always present when an a-c heater is employed.

A discussion of the interesting question as to what happens to the second sound at temperatures below 1°K is deferred to a later chapter.

[1] V. Peshkov, *J. Exptl. Theoret. Phys.* (*U.S.S.R.*), **18**:867 (1948).

[2] N. Kurti and J. McIntosh, Proceedings of the Paris Conference, International Union of Pure and Applied Physics, 1955.

[3] The entropy of certain salts, such as iron ammonium alum, is diminished by applying a magnetic field. Hence in a sinusoidal field the temperature of the salt will alternately increase and decrease every half-cycle.

CHAPTER 5

Phonons and Rotons

SOME CLASSICAL WAVE THEOREMS

Consider a linear chain of particles, each of mass m, the distance between each pair being a. There are $(N + 1)$ such particles; the first is numbered 0 and the last N. Suppose the forces between particles obey Hooke's law and we consider nearest neighbor interactions only. The length of the chain is $L = Na$.

Further, let us restrain the motion of any particle to a direction along the chain. If any particle is thus displaced, we shall expect intuitively that such displacement will propagate as a wave; let the displacement of the nth particle, at any time, be U_n. This particle will experience two forces, in opposite directions, due to its neighbors, whose displacements will be U_{n+1} and U_{n-1}, respectively (Fig. 37). Calling these forces f_{n+1} and f_{n-1}, respectively, we have

$$f_{n+1} = \beta(U_{n+1} + a - U_n - a)$$
$$f_{n-1} = \beta(U_n + a - U_{n-1} - a)$$

where β is the Hooke's law constant. Hence the equation of motion of the nth particle will be

$$m\ddot{U}_n = f_{n+1} - f_{n-1} = \beta(U_{n+1} + U_{n-1} - 2U_n) \tag{1}$$

Our expectation is that the motion will be a wave; hence we seek a "plane" wave solution for Eq. (1), i.e.,

$$U_n = A e^{i(\omega t - kna)} \tag{2}$$

Here $\omega = 2\pi$ (frequency) and $k = 2\pi/$wavelength, and we note that na is the equilibrium distance from the first particle or what we should call x in the usual elementary formula for a wave.

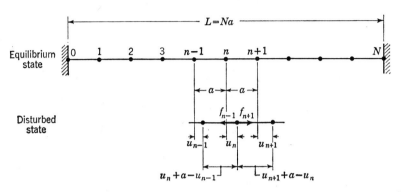

FIG. 37. A linear chain of $(N + 1)$ particles, of which the end ones are clamped, leaving $(N - 1)$ free to move.

Substituting (2) into (1), we get

$$-\omega^2 = \frac{\beta}{m} (e^{-ika} + e^{ika} - 2)$$

But
$$e^{-ika} + e^{ika} - 2 = (e^{-i(ka/2)} - e^{i(ka/2)})^2$$

$$= -4 \sin^2 \left(\frac{ka}{2} \right)$$

Hence
$$\omega = \pm \sqrt{\frac{4\beta}{m}} \sin \frac{ka}{2} \qquad (3)$$

Hence (2) is a solution of (1) if, and only if, the condition (3) is obeyed. The two signs involved merely mean that the wave is propagated either right or left.

Clearly, the sine has a maximum real value when its argument is such as to make it unity, i.e.,

$$\omega = \omega_{\max} \quad \text{when} \quad \frac{ka}{2} = \frac{\pi}{2} \qquad (4)$$

and remembering the definition of k (the wave number), this means

$$\lambda_{\min} = 2a \qquad (5)$$

Thus there is a maximum frequency (or minimum wavelength) beyond which no wave propagation is possible.[1]

This situation is entirely different from that in a "continuum," wherein every frequency up to infinity is possible, and arises because of the "atomistic" nature of our model. As a matter of fact, if we consider the case where $\lambda \gg a$, then it is easy to show that the phase velocity V $(= \omega/k)$ becomes independent of k; i.e., the waves are nondispersive, as is the case in a continuum.

Now if the first and last particles in the chain are clamped, we shall obtain reflections there and set up a pattern of standing waves. As is usual, we use linear combinations of the solution (2) and obtain standing waves of the form

$$U_n = A e^{i\omega t} \sin kna \qquad (6)$$

This must obey the boundary conditions

$$U_n = 0 \qquad n = 0 \qquad n = N$$

that is, $\qquad kNa = S\pi \qquad$ or $\qquad k = \dfrac{S\pi}{L} \qquad (7)$

where $S = 1, 2, 3 \ldots$ Hence Eq. (6) becomes

$$U_n = A e^{i\omega t} \sin \frac{S\pi na}{L}$$
$$= A e^{i\omega t} \sin \left(\frac{S}{N} n\pi \right) \qquad (8)$$

The first mode corresponds to $S = 1$ and the last one to $S = N - 1$, since Eq. (8) vanishes for $S = N$; i.e., there is no motion. Thus there are $(N - 1)$ permissible modes, which is equal to the total number of particles *free to move* in the chain. Stated another way, this means that there is one mode per degree of freedom. This is a simple case of a very general result characteristic also of two- and three-dimensional lattices.

---

[1] For frequencies higher than ω_{max}, k becomes imaginary. Accordingly, if we write

$$k = -2\pi i \alpha \qquad \omega > \omega_{max}$$

where α is a real positive number (dimensions in reciprocal centimeters), then Eq. (2) becomes

$$U_n = A e^{i\omega t} e^{-2\pi \alpha na}$$

i.e., the vibrations decay exponentially along the chain, the quantity $2\pi\alpha$ being the attenuation coefficient.

We turn now to a problem concerning plane waves in a continuum which is capable of transmitting only one kind of wave, say of the compressional type.   Imagine a cube in this medium each of whose sides is L, and suppose that a wave on reaching any boundary is perfectly reflected.   According to the laws of optics, (1) the angles of incidence and reflection shall be equal, (2) the incident and reflected rays and the normal to the reflecting plane shall be coplanar, and (3) the frequency remains unchanged.

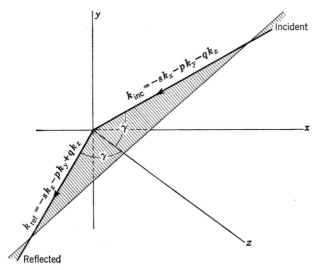

FIG. 38. Reflection of an arbitrarily directed wave at the xy plane.

The equation of a plane wave arbitrarily directed in space is

$$\psi = A e^{i(\omega t - \mathbf{k} \cdot \mathbf{r})} \tag{9}$$

where $\mathbf{r}$ is a position vector of any point on the wave front and $\mathbf{k}$ is the wave-number vector pointing in a direction perpendicular thereto. The scalar product would be equal to the usual kx in the one-dimensional case.

Referring to Fig. 38, let this wave suffer a reflection at a cube face located in the xy plane.   Now

$$\mathbf{r} = \mathbf{s}x + \mathbf{p}y + \mathbf{q}z$$

where $\mathbf{s}$, $\mathbf{p}$, and $\mathbf{q}$ are unit vectors in the x, y, and z directions, respectively.   As Fig. 38 shows,

$$\mathbf{k}_{\text{inc}} = -\mathbf{s}k_x - \mathbf{p}k_y - \mathbf{q}k_z$$

and

$$\mathbf{k}_{\text{refl}} = -\mathbf{s}k_x - \mathbf{p}k_y + \mathbf{q}k_z$$

Now the wavefronts of the incident and reflected waves will overlap, and their displacements at such points will be additive, i.e.,

$$
\begin{aligned}
\psi_1 = \psi_{\text{inc}} + \psi_{\text{refl}} &= A e^{i\omega t}(e^{i(k_x x + k_y y + k_z z)} + e^{i(k_x x + k_y y - k_z z)}) \\
&= A e^{i(\omega t + k_x x + k_y y)}(e^{ik_z z} + e^{-ik_z z}) \\
&= 2A \cos (k_z z) e^{i(\omega t + k_x x + k_y y)}
\end{aligned}
\tag{10}
$$

Equation (10) represents a wave confined solely to the xy plane but with amplitude "modulated" in the z direction. The period (i.e., the distance between nodes) of this modulation is

$$
\frac{\pi}{k \cos \gamma}
\tag{11}
$$

where α, β, and γ are the angles which the incident ray makes to the x, y, and z directions, respectively.

Now ψ_1 will suffer a reflection at the xz plane, and precisely as before will give rise to a wave

$$
\psi_2 = 4A \cos k_z z \cos (k_y y) e^{i(\omega t + k_x x)}
\tag{12}
$$

and the above wave will finally suffer a reflection at a yz plane, giving rise finally to

$$
\psi_3 = 8A \cos k_z z \cos k_y y \cos (k_x x) e^{i\omega t}
\tag{13}
$$

Since we have now exhausted all possibilities for reflections, Eq. (13) represents the final standing-wave pattern in our three-dimensional continuum.

Now our postulated condition that we have perfect reflections means that we shall have nodes at each cube face; i.e., there must be an integral number of periods in each length L, i.e., referring to Eq. (11), we get

$$
S_1 = \frac{L}{\pi/(k \cos \alpha)} \qquad S_2 = \frac{L}{\pi/(k \cos \beta)} \qquad S_3 = \frac{L}{\pi/(k \cos \gamma)}
\tag{14}
$$

where S_1, S_2, and S_3 are integers. Squaring these and adding, we obtain

$$
S_1{}^2 + S_2{}^2 + S_3{}^2 = \frac{k^2 L^2}{\pi^2} (\cos^2 \alpha + \cos^2 \beta + \cos^2 \gamma) = \frac{k^2 L^2}{\pi^2}
\tag{15}
$$

Or, in terms of wave velocity u and frequency $\nu = \omega/2\pi$, this becomes

$$
S_1{}^2 + S_2{}^2 + S_3{}^2 = \frac{4L^2}{u^2} \nu^2
\tag{16}
$$

Our next task is to compute a mode distribution function; i.e., we wish to count the number of modes, dn, whose frequencies lie in the

interval from ν to $(\nu + d\nu)$.   To do this, we note that any combination
of the three integers S_1, S_2, and S_3 defines a vibration pattern or mode,
as Eqs. (13) plus (14) show.   Thus $S_1 = 2$, $S_2 = 1$, $S_3 = 4$ is one; and
$S_1 = 1$, $S_2 = 2$, and $S_3 = 4$ is another.   In fact, if we plot S_1, S_2, and
S_3 along each of three mutually perpendicular axes, the modes will be
represented by the corners of a lattice made up of elementary cubes (or
unit cells, in the language of crystallography), the volume of each being
unity.   Figure 39 illustrates this for the simpler (to draw) case of two
dimensions.

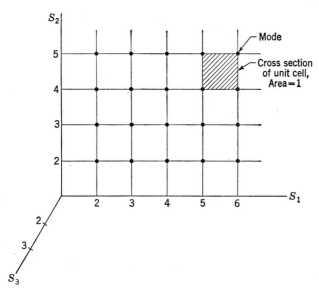

FIG. 39. A plane through the S space showing some modes.   In three dimensions
the unit cell has a volume of 1.   Each of the eight modes per cell is shared by eight
other cells.   Hence there is one mode per unit cell.

The square of the radius vector, R^2, from the origin to any mode
designated, in general, by the group of numbers S_1, S_2, and S_3 is clearly

$$R^2 = S_1{}^2 + S_2{}^2 + S_3{}^2 = \frac{4L^2}{u^2}\, \nu^2 \tag{17}$$

Further, any unit cell corner, or mode, is shared by a total of eight
unit cells.   And since each unit cell possesses eight corners, this means
that each unit cell (volume = 1) "owns" just one mode.
    The above facts permit us now to compute the desired distribution
function approximately; the larger the total number of modes, the

better is the approximation. And we also notice that negative values of the numbers S_1, S_2, and S_3 do not, according to Eq. (13), lead to any new modes. Hence we shall confine our counting to the first quadrant in our S plot. Thus

$$dn = \frac{1}{8} \frac{\text{volume between } R \text{ and } R + dR}{\text{volume per mode}}$$

$$= \frac{1}{8} \frac{4\pi R^2 \, dR}{1}$$

$$= \frac{1}{8} 4\pi \frac{4L^2}{u^2} \nu^2 \frac{2L}{u} \, d\nu \qquad \text{[using Eq. (17)]}$$

$$= \frac{4\pi L^3}{u^3} \nu^2 \, d\nu \qquad\qquad\qquad\qquad\qquad (18)$$

To repeat, the above is only an approximation since we have tacitly assumed the density of modes in the S space to be infinitely large ("everywhere dense").

SPECIFIC HEATS

The physicists of the nineteenth century had a most pleasant approach to the problem presented by the specific heats of solids. It was nice because it was both simple and plausible. They argued that, in a solid composed of N atoms each with three degrees of transla- tional freedom, kT of thermal energy ought to be assigned to each degree of freedom. In a gas it was $\frac{1}{2}kT$, as their kinetic theory required; but unlike a gas, the atoms in the solid possessed potential energy in addition to kinetic energy of motion, so it seemed plausible to give each part its share.

The result indicated a specific heat independent of temperature, the same for all solids and amounting to about 6 cal/mole °C. And it seemed very reasonable, since the physics of low temperatures had not been invented and so no one really knew if the specific heat of a solid was temperature dependent or not. More important, the empirically determined specific heats of many solids around room temperature turned out to be not too far removed from the figure 6 cal/mole °C (the law of Dulong and Petit).

But in the closing years of the nineteenth century Dewar succeeded in liquefying hydrogen and (as we would say today) in quantity. He also invented the Dewar flask, an indispensable tool for cryogenics. The result of this was that by 1910 the specific heats of some solids had been investigated down to 15°K. And the results all showed that these were far from temperature independent; rather, the specific heats seemed to be approaching zero at the absolute zero, albeit having nearly the Dulong-Petit value at room temperature.

Einstein, to most of us, suggests relativity, but he did great things in several fields of physics. And among these must certainly be counted the next step—the application of Planck's quantum, at the time new and highly controversial, to the specific-heat problem. His approach was very direct; he assumed each of the $3N$ degrees of freedom to be equivalent to a single frequency (ν_E) or mode and the energy of any such mode to be given by that of a Planck oscillator of the same frequency. Since the latter is

$$\frac{h\nu}{e^{h\nu/kT} - 1}$$

the specific heat would be

$$C = 3N \frac{\partial}{\partial T} \left(\frac{h\nu_E}{e^{h\nu_E/kT} - 1} \right) \tag{19}$$

Expression (19) limits at $C = 0$, $T \to 0$, and $C = 3kN \cong 6$ cal/mole °C at $T \to \infty$. Equation (19) contains an unknown parameter ν_E and hence cannot of itself yield a numerical value. It can, however, be "fitted" to the empirical data by determining ν_E from the measured specific heat at one temperature. When this is done, using good data, it is seen that expression (19) is only order-of-magnitude correct—a mighty step in the right direction, but not quite enough. Nonetheless, it showed Einstein, and those who followed him, that specific heat was a quantum phenomenon—as important a demonstration, in its way, as the Rutherford-Bohr atom.

Why is the Einstein formula so close to reality and yet so far? The answer, at least to those of us who benefit from nearly half a century of thinking on the subject, seems pretty obvious. It lies in the assumption that all the vibrational modes have a common frequency. And when we try to correct this obvious fallacy, we run into considerable difficulty.

At first sight it would seem that, having deduced the frequency distribution in a continuum [Eq. (18)], the computation of the energy and hence the specific heat in a real solid should be easy. However, even if we treat the solid as a continuum and use therefore the classical theory of elasticity, we are at once confronted with several troubles. First, we then have three types of waves—one compressional [as was assumed in Eq. (18)] and two transverse, polarized at right angles. In addition, the transverse and compressional waves have different velocities. If we count the modes due to these, in addition to the longitudinal one, then Eq. (18) becomes

$$dn = 4\pi L^3 \left(\frac{1}{u_l^3} + \frac{2}{u_t^3}\right) \nu^2 \, d\nu \tag{20}$$

However, a much more serious difficulty arises because of the boundary conditions. In deducing (18) we assumed, in effect, a perfectly rigid and smooth boundary. In a real solid this could not exist; in this case, for instance, a compressional wave falling on a boundary gives a reflected compressive wave but, in addition, excites a transverse reflection.

Again a continuum gives an infinity of modes, whereas a lattice of atoms (as our simple linear chain shows) does not. Obviously we cannot deal with an infinity of modes; we must "cut off" the frequency spectrum at some maximum frequency corresponding to a minimum allowable wavelength.

In the linear chain we saw that there were the same number of modes as there were particles in the chain which were free to move. It turns out that, for the three-dimensional lattice containing N particles in volume $V = L^3$, there are $3N$ modes—N for the compressional waves and $2N$ for the transverse. And in addition, we must have the same minimum wavelength and hence different cutoff frequencies for the two types.

But the above is the result of later work, and Debye, in his famous paper of 1912 on specific heats, did not know this. Consequently, he assumed that the frequency of cutoff would be such that the sum of all the modes up to this frequency would be $3N$, using the frequency distribution of Eq. (20), i.e.,

$$3N = \gamma \int_0^{\nu_{\text{max}}} \nu^2 \, d\nu \qquad \gamma = 4\pi V \left(\frac{1}{u_l^3} + \frac{2}{u_t^3}\right)$$

or

$$\nu_{\text{max}} = \left(\frac{9N}{\gamma}\right)^{\frac{1}{3}} \tag{21}$$

and hence

$$C = \gamma \frac{\partial}{\partial T} \int_0^{\nu_m} \frac{h\nu^3 \, d\nu}{e^{h\nu/kT} - 1} = k\gamma \int_0^{\nu_m} \frac{(h\nu/kT)^2 e^{h\nu/kT}}{(e^{h\nu/kT} - 1)^2} \nu^2 \, d\nu \tag{22}$$

Following Debye, we define a "characteristic temperature" θ:

$$h\nu_{\text{max}} = k\theta$$

Recalling that $\lambda_{\min} \sim 2a$ and considering the case, say, of copper, we find

$$a \sim 3.6 \text{ A}$$
$$u_l \sim 3,600 \text{ m/sec}$$
giving $$\nu_{max} \sim 5 \times 10^{12} \text{ vib/sec}$$

Writing $x = h\nu/kT$, we see that the upper limit of the integral in Eq. (22) can be approximated as infinity, especially if the temperature T is low, i.e.,

$$C \cong \gamma \frac{k^4 T^3}{h^3} \int_0^\infty \frac{x^4 e^x \, dx}{(e^x - 1)^2}$$

But

$$\int_0^\infty \frac{x^4 e^x \, dx}{(e^x - 1)^2} = \frac{4}{15} \pi^4$$

and

$$\gamma = \frac{9Nh^3}{k^3 \theta^3}$$

and so, finally,

$$C \cong \frac{12}{5} \pi^4 k N \left(\frac{T}{\theta}\right)^3 \tag{23}$$

This is Debye's celebrated "T^3 law," valid at the lowest temperatures. The specific heat (per mole) according to Eq. (23) varies from substance to substance solely because of the variation in θ, which, in turn, depends on their elastic constants; and, in general, the value of C computed from Eq. (23) is in excellent agreement with the experimental values for many simple solids.[1] In addition, the Debye temperature θ is a number which turns out to be temperature independent, or nearly so, in many cases.

In 1939 Pickard and Simon investigated the specific heat of He II in the temperature range 0.25 to 1°K and, most surprisingly, found that the result obeyed Eq. (23) below about 0.8°K with a $\theta \cong 15.5$°K. This pioneer experiment, which has since been improved and confirmed by others, was a milestone in our understanding of superfluidity.[2]

LANDAU'S THEORY (1941)[3]

The Normal Component of He II. So far we have advanced no theoretical basis for the set of postulates written down in an earlier

---

[1] For many metals the measured specific heat at lowest temperatures contains, in addition, a small term linear in temperature. This is due to the conduction electrons.

[2] The best presently available measurements give $C = 0.02T^3$ joules/g °K in the temperature region below 0.6°K. (H. C. Kramers, "Progress in Low Temperature Physics," vol. II, Interscience Publishers, Inc., New York, 1957.)

[3] L. Landau, *J. Phys.* (*U.S.S.R.*), **5**:71 (1941).

chapter. The experimental evidence in support of them is so good, however, that it seems certain that any successful theory of He II must, in one way or another, lead to the same or similar propositions.

A fundamental part of the whole problem consists in dividing He II into two fluids, each with separate properties, and permitting the two to coexist, in some fashion, at all temperatures lying between absolute zero and the lambda point. At 0°K all the He II will be in one state, and as we apply some heat and raise the temperature, the normal-component fluid will commence to form. What can we imagine to be the nature of this normal fluid?

It occurred to a number of physicists, including of course Landau, that Debye excitations (phonons) might, in reality, be what we call the normal component. Now a phonon is a somewhat intangible thing, difficult to visualize, just as is a photon and for the same reasons. The photon, in a sense, is an experimental thing. It was forced upon us by the photoelectric-effect experiments and by Compton's work, and despite the wave theory of light which accounted so beautifully for a complex of phenomena. Let us say that, in the hands of Einstein and Debye, the phonon was similarly forced on us by the experiments with specific heats at low temperature.

Now all through our previous discussion we have been tacitly assuming the normal component to be a more tangible thing. We have talked as though a certain fraction of the He II atoms were in the normal state. But if we accept the idea of phonons, this is certainly untrue—*all* the He II atoms form the normal fluid. This difficulty, not always entirely realized by some writers, arises because we have, with Einstein and Debye, turned aside from classical physics with its comfortable models and commenced a journey into the misty regions of quantum mechanics.

Let us now, following Landau, attempt to compute a quantity which we shall call $\rho_n{}^{\text{ph}}$ and which, mathematically, will correspond to the "density of the normal component." To do this we shall have to visualize a sort of "gas" of these excitations and imagine all the "particles" of this gas to be moving with a small constant velocity u. Next we compute the momentum $\langle p \rangle$ of the whole assembly (in the u direction) for 1 cm³ of this gas, remembering, of course, that each particle will have a random momentum due to temperature, in addition to this drift momentum. If it turns out (as indeed it will) that this momentum is linear in u, then the number multiplying u will be the effective mass of 1 cm³ of excitations, i.e., the desired quantity $\rho_n{}^{\text{ph}}$.

Clearly, the above constitutes an exercise in statistical mechanics, and we must next decide what statistics to use. Since the Debye modes each have the mean energy of a Planck oscillator (photons), the statistics will have to be Bose-Einstein.

Consider, for the moment, a gas of such excitations possessing no drift velocity. Each particle will have a random thermal momentum p_0. According to de Broglie's ideas, its energy ε_0 will be

$$\varepsilon_0 = h\nu_0 = \frac{h}{\lambda_0} c = pc \tag{24}$$

where c is the velocity of the compressional wave, i.e., of first sound.[1]

Now if we denote by E_{ph} the total phonon energy of a collection of modes, we shall have, using Eq. (20),

$$E_{ph} = \gamma \int_0^\infty \frac{h\nu^3 \, d\nu}{e^{h\nu/kT} - 1}$$

And since

$$\varepsilon_0 = h\nu = pc \qquad \gamma = \frac{4\pi V}{c^3} \qquad \beta = \frac{1}{kT}$$

this becomes

$$E_{ph} = \frac{4\pi V}{h^3} c \int_0^\infty \frac{p^3 \, dp}{e^{\beta\varepsilon_0} - 1} \tag{25}$$

Now, by the use of Bose statistics, the above expression (25) can be deduced in a neater way. In these statistics the phase space whose volume element is $dp_x \, dp_y \, dp_z \, dx \, dy \, dz$ is divided into cells of volume h^3, and the number of particles whose momenta lie in the range p to $(p + dp)$ is given by

$$dn = \frac{1}{e^{\beta\varepsilon_0} - 1} \frac{dp_x \, dp_y \, dp_z \, dx \, dy \, dz}{h^3} \tag{26}$$

The extreme right-hand term of (26) is the number of states in the given range of momentum, and it is multiplied by an expression giving the probability of finding a particle of energy ε_0 in any state. Hence

$$E_{ph} = \int \varepsilon_0 \, dn = \iiiiii \frac{\varepsilon_0 \, dp_x \, dp_y \, dp_z \, dx \, dy \, dz}{(e^{\beta\varepsilon_0} - 1)h^3}$$

$$= \frac{V}{h^3} \iiint \frac{\varepsilon_0}{e^{\beta\varepsilon_0} - 1} \, dp_x \, dp_y \, dp_z \tag{27}$$

Now if we write the momenta in terms of spherical coordinates (Fig. 41 shows our notation), we shall have

$$dp_x \, dp_y \, dp_z = dp \, p \sin\theta \, d\varphi \, p \, d\theta$$

[1] Ignoring small viscosity effects, there are no transverse waves in a liquid.

and expression (27) then reads

$$E_{ph} = \frac{V}{h^3} \int_0^p \int_0^\pi \int_0^{2\pi} \frac{pc}{e^{\beta \varepsilon_0} - 1} p^2 \, dp \, \sin \theta \, d\theta \, d\varphi$$

$$= \frac{4\pi V c}{h^3} \int_0^p \frac{p^3 \, dp}{e^{\beta \varepsilon_0} - 1}$$

which is identical to expression (25).

We have digressed a bit from our main purpose, which is to compute the momentum of an assembly of phonons each of which has a small constant drift velocity u relative to an observer at rest. Now because

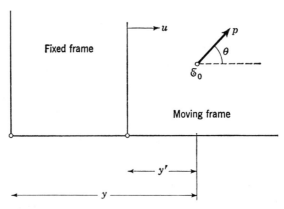

FIG. 40. Notation for phonon possessing drift velocity u relative to observer at rest. The velocity is taken in the y direction.

of the wave properties of the particles, this observer will see a different wavelength than would be observed were there no drift velocity. This, so to speak, is the quantum analogue of the Doppler effect. This, in turn, means that the momenta h/λ and hence the energy pc will be different.

In order to compute this new phonon energy ε, we follow a scheme originally due to Dingle.[1] To an observer in the moving frame the wave function of the particle would look like

$$\psi = A e^{\frac{1}{ih}(\varepsilon_0 t' - \mathbf{p} \cdot \mathbf{y}')}$$

this being a plane wave of frequency ε_0/h and wavelength h/p. Figure 40 shows our notation. Now relative to the fixed frame

$$y = y' + ut \qquad t = t'$$

[1] R. B. Dingle, *Phil. Mag. Suppl.*, **1**(2): 137 (1952).

that is, $\psi = A \exp \left\{ \dfrac{1}{i\hbar} \left[\varepsilon_0 t - \mathbf{p} \cdot (\mathbf{y} - \mathbf{u}t) \right] \right\}$

$\qquad\qquad = A \exp \left\{ \dfrac{1}{i\hbar} \left[(\varepsilon_0 + \mathbf{p} \cdot \mathbf{u})t - \mathbf{p} \cdot \mathbf{y} \right] \right\}$

Thus relative to the observer at rest the energy ε of the particle is

$$\varepsilon = \varepsilon_0 + \mathbf{p} \cdot \mathbf{u} \qquad\qquad (28)$$

Thus the distribution function becomes

$$\frac{dn}{d\tau} = \frac{V}{h^3} \frac{1}{e^{\beta(\varepsilon - \mathbf{p} \cdot \mathbf{u})} - 1} \qquad\qquad (29)$$

where $d\tau = dp_x \, dp_y \, dp_z$

Now each phonon will have a component of momentum in the y direc-

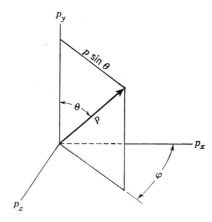

FIG. 41. Notation for spherical coordinates.

tion (cf. Fig. 40) of $p \cos \theta$ and so, since $\mathbf{p} \cdot \mathbf{u} = pu \cos \theta$, we have

$$\langle p \rangle = \int p \cos \theta \, dn$$

$$\langle p \rangle = \frac{V}{h^3} \int_0^\infty \int_0^\pi \int_0^{2\pi} \frac{p \cos \theta}{e^{\beta(\varepsilon - pu \cos \theta)} - 1} p^2 \, dp \sin \theta \, d\theta \, d\varphi \qquad (30)$$

We have made the assumption that u is small, which means $u \ll c$, and we now proceed to expand

$$f(u) = \frac{1}{e^{\beta(\varepsilon - pu \cos \theta)} - 1}$$

using Maclaurin expansion and neglecting squares and higher terms in *u.* This gives

$$f(u) \cong \frac{1}{e^{\beta \varepsilon} - 1} + u \frac{\beta p \, \cos \theta e^{\beta \varepsilon}}{(e^{\beta \varepsilon} - 1)^2}$$

Substituting this into expression (30) gives

$$\langle p \rangle = \frac{V}{h^3} \int_0^\infty \int_0^\pi \int_0^{2\pi} \frac{p^3 \, dp \, \sin \theta \, \cos \theta \, d\theta \, d\varphi}{e^{\beta \varepsilon} - 1}$$

$$+ \frac{\beta V}{h^3} u \int_0^\infty \int_0^\pi \int_0^{2\pi} \frac{e^{\beta \varepsilon} p^4 \, dp \, \sin \theta \, \cos^2 \theta \, d\theta \, d\varphi}{(e^{\beta \varepsilon} - 1)^2}$$

The first integral on the right-hand side vanishes since

$$\int_0^\pi \sin \theta \, \cos \theta \, d\theta = 0$$

Also $\int_0^\pi \sin \theta \, \cos^2 \theta \, d\theta = \frac{2}{3}$ and $\int_0^{2\pi} d\varphi = 2\pi$

Hence $\langle p \rangle = \frac{4}{3} \frac{\pi \beta V}{h^3} u \int_0^\infty \frac{e^{\beta \varepsilon} p^4 \, dp}{(e^{\beta \varepsilon} - 1)^2}$

Now $\varepsilon = \varepsilon_0 + pu \, \cos \theta$ and $\varepsilon_0 = pc$

Hence $\varepsilon = p(c + u \, \cos \theta) \cong pc$ $u \ll c$

Hence, finally,

$$\langle p \rangle = \frac{4}{3} \frac{\pi \beta V}{h^3} u \int_0^\infty \frac{e^{\beta pc} p^4 \, dp}{(e^{\beta pc} - 1)^2}$$

Calling this integral J and integrating by parts, we obtain

$$J = -\frac{1}{\beta c} \left[\frac{p^4}{e^{\beta pc} - 1} \right]_0^\infty + \frac{4}{\beta c} \int_0^\infty \frac{p^3 \, dp}{e^{\beta pc} - 1}$$

The first term vanishes at both limits, and recalling Eq. (25), we have therefore

$$J = \frac{h^3 E_{\mathrm{ph}}}{\pi \beta V c^2}$$

Hence, finally,

$$\langle p \rangle = \left(\frac{4}{3} \frac{E_{\mathrm{ph}}}{c^2} \right) u \qquad (31)$$

Now $C = \frac{\partial E_{\mathrm{ph}}}{\partial T}$

and, at the lowest temperatures, the measurements give

$$C = 0.02 T^3 \ \text{joules/g} \ ^\circ\text{K}$$

Thus $E_{\mathrm{ph}} = 5 \times 10^4 T^4$ ergs/g

$$= 5 \times 10^4 T^4 \rho \qquad \text{ergs/cm}^3$$

where ρ is the density of He II.

Hence, from expression (31), the "effective phonon mass" in 1 cm³ of He II ($\rho_n{}^{\text{ph}}$) is

$$\frac{\rho_n{}^{\text{ph}}}{\rho} = \frac{2 \times 10^5}{3c^2} \, T^4$$

And since $c \cong 240$ m/sec, we get

$$\frac{\rho_n{}^{\text{ph}}}{\rho} \cong 1.2 \times 10^{-4} T^4 \qquad (32)$$

Thus at 1°K the normal-component fraction, if it were due solely to phonons, would be, according to (32), of the order of 10^{-2} per cent. Admittedly this is pushing the extrapolation somewhat, since the above analysis is restricted to, at best, temperatures below about 0.6°K. Nevertheless, by any standard, this is much too small as compared with Andronikashvili's results.

Andronikashvili's measurements extend only to about 1°K, and it would, in point of fact, be quite impossible to use his method much below this temperature. The only other way to obtain experimental data is to deduce them from second sound measurements. Unfortunately, second sound measurements much below 1°K are, for reasons which will emerge subsequently, none too reliable. Despite this, and in view of the now well-established specific-heat data which clearly show a T^3 law at the lowest temperatures, it appears quite certain that, in the vicinity of the absolute zero, the normal component of He II is due to phonon excitations.

The above suggests very strongly that there must be an additional mechanism which, while negligible at the lowest temperatures, begins to make itself felt, ever more strongly, commencing at a temperature around 0.6°K. This other, and additional, type of quantum excitation was named by Landau, its discoverer, a "roton."

We have been at some pains to point out that, from the classical way of thinking, the phonon is a somewhat intangible entity. To those with some reasonable acquaintance with modern physics, however, this is untrue; the phonon is as real as the electron. Such has not been the case with the roton, at least until very recently. As eminent a physicist as the late F. London, for instance, was most loath to accept them, saying " . . . it is not possible to give a clear, even if approximate, definition of the roton."[1] Nonetheless, there is a growing body of evidence, both experimental and theoretical, for their existence.

[1] F. London, "Superfluids," vol. II, p. 89, John Wiley & Sons, Inc., New York, 1954.

Landau, in the famous 1941 paper which we are discussing, was untroubled by such doubts as London subsequently raised. He thought that a liquid, as distinct from a solid, would have to be capable of some sort of rotational or vortex motions. Macroscopically this is obvious, but to postulate elementary quantized excitations of this nature and unique to He II is much less so, and this was the base of the difficulty in giving a precise meaning to the entity.[1]

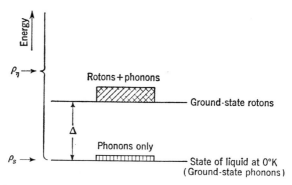

FIG. 42. Landau spectrum for the normal component of He II. Shaded blocks show occupied states in the vicinity of 1°K.

This lack of definition reflects itself in the postulated energy spectrum which Landau proposed, viz.,

$$\varepsilon_{\text{rot}} = \frac{p^2}{2\mu} + \Delta$$

Here Δ is a postulated energy gap between the roton and phonon ground states. This is necessary to assure that the ensuing ρ_n^{rot}/ρ fraction will decrease exponentially with temperature and thus become negligible at the lowest temperatures,[2] as our previous deliberations have shown to be necessary. The quantity μ is an "effective mass" for the roton, and absolute magnitudes for neither μ nor Δ emerged from the

---

[1] Some years ago, the Yale theoretician L. Onsager, when asked to define the roton, called it "the ghost of a vanishing vortex ring."

[2] We must continually bear in mind that

$$\frac{\rho_n}{\rho} = \frac{\rho_n^{\text{ph}}}{\rho} + \frac{\rho_n^{\text{rot}}}{\rho}$$

theory.[1] We notice that the term $p^2/2\mu$ is merely the classical kinetic energy of a particle with momentum p and mass μ, thus reflecting the uncertainty of the real nature of the roton. So to speak, this ignorance is all lumped into the factor μ. This uncertainty is further reflected in the fact that, some years later, Landau modified the roton spectrum to

$$\varepsilon_{\text{rot}} = \frac{(p - p_0)^2}{2\mu} + \Delta \tag{33}$$

where p_0 is a constant. He did this purely for the purpose of achieving a better "fit" to the then available experimental evidence. The Landau spectrum is illustrated in Fig. 42 and, more quantitatively, in Fig. 43.

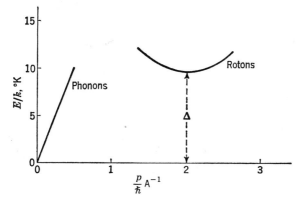

FIG. 43. A plot of energy versus momentum for the excitations in He II, showing the two branches of the Landau spectrum.

We now have the problem of computing the roton contribution ρ_n^{rot} and, as before, have to decide the proper statistics. Because of the uncertainty of the model, this is not immediately apparent; probably they are Bose, as befits a "spinless" particle. However, owing now to the presence of the large gap Δ in the energy term, the exponential in Eq. (26) is much larger than was the case with phonons, and we can neglect unity in comparison. This converts the statistics into something like Boltzmann. Besides this, the calculation is rendered easier by the fact that, unlike the phonons, we have given the roton a "built-in" mass μ which appears explicitly in the energy term. Referring back to Eq. (26) and in view of the above, the number of rotons

[1] On a purely dimensional argument, $\Delta \sim \rho^{2/3}\hbar^2 m^{-5/3}$, ρ and m being the density of the liquid and the mass of the helium atom (cf. Dingle, *loc. cit.*)

N_{rot} will be given by[1]

$$N_{\text{rot}} = \frac{V}{h^3} \int_0^\infty \int_0^\pi \int_0^{2\pi} e^{-\beta(p^2/(2\mu)+\Delta)} \, p^2 \, dp \, \sin\theta \, d\theta \, d\varphi$$

$$= \frac{4\pi V}{h^3} e^{-\beta\Delta} \int_0^\infty e^{\frac{-\beta p^2}{2\mu}} \, p^2 \, dp$$

$$= V\left(\frac{2\pi\mu k T}{h^2}\right)^{3/2} e^{-\Delta/kT} \qquad (34)$$

The above expression is dimensionless, as it should be, provided μ is in grams, Δ in ergs, and V in cubic centimeters. Since we require the

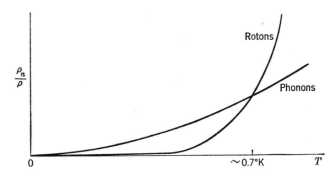

FIG. 44. Temperature dependence of the roton and phonon contributions to the normal component. This is merely schematic, since the ratio of the two densities at 0.2°K, for instance, is $\sim 10^{-12}$.

mass of rotons per cubic centimeter (ρ_n^{rot}) and since each roton has a mass μ, then clearly

$$\rho_n^{\text{rot}} = N_{\text{rot}}\mu \qquad V = 1$$

or

$$\frac{\rho_n^{\text{rot}}}{\rho} = \frac{\mu}{\rho}\left(\frac{2\pi\mu k T}{h^2}\right)^{3/2} e^{-\Delta/kT} \qquad (35)$$

Figure 44, which is illustrative and not drawn to scale, shows the temperature variation of the two excitations in the region below 1°K where, because of the ideal-gas nature of the excitations, the theory most accurately applies.

We have now computed the full value of ρ_n/ρ, but this contains two[2] unknown parameters, namely, Δ and μ. Landau elected to evaluate these by computing the combined specific heat of the two excitations

[1] We use the original formulation of the roton energy spectrum for reasons of simplicity. The argument is not materially altered by doing so.

[2] Three if we had used the later form for the roton energy spectrum.

and comparing the result with the empirical data. The specific heat for phonons we already have, and so it remains to compute that for rotons. Calling the energy of the rotons (in volume V) E_{rot}, we have

$$E_{rot} = \sum N_{rot} \left(\frac{p^2}{2\mu} + \Delta \right)$$

that is, $\quad E_{rot} = \frac{4\pi V}{h^3} \int_0^\infty e^{-p^2/2\mu kT} e^{-\Delta/kT} \left(\frac{p^2}{2\mu} + \Delta \right) p^2\, dp$

And since $C_{rot} = \partial E_{rot}/\partial T$ and since the limits of the above integral do not contain T, we may simply differentiate under the integral sign, and, although the algebra is cumbersome, we find that all the resulting integrals are standard forms. The result is

$$C_{rot} = \frac{V}{h^3} (2\pi\mu k)^{3/2} \Delta^2 \frac{e^{-\Delta/kT}}{kT^{1/2}} \left[1 + 3\left(\frac{kT}{\Delta} \right) + \frac{15}{4} \left(\frac{kT}{\Delta} \right)^2 \right] \quad (36)$$

Upon comparing the combined computed specific heats of the two types of excitations with the experimental values of his day for He II, Landau[1] found $\Delta/k \sim 8$ to $9°$K and $\mu \sim 7$ to 8 helium atom masses.

With this, Landau had achieved an analytic function of the temperature for the ratio ρ_n/ρ. If this is put equal to unity, then the resulting value of the temperature should be that of the λ point. The result gave $T_\lambda = 2.3°$K, in remarkable agreement with the experimental value. This, however, is rather fortuitous since at high roton densities roton-roton interactions would likely become important, and we have not considered this in the theory.[2]

The later form of the energy spectrum, containing one more adjustable constant, gives, as we have mentioned, a better fit to the modern

---

[1] At the time he had no data which he considered reliable either for the specific heat of He II in the phonon region or for the velocity of first sound. A. Migdal had computed the latter from some 1936 compressibility measurements, getting the not-too-bad value of 250 m/sec. With this the Debye temperature was computable [Eq. (21)] and thence the phonon specific heat from Eq. (23).

[2] We have ignored an important, even crucial, point with regard to the behavior of the normal-fluid component as theoretically deduced; namely, would such an assembly of excitations possess a viscosity coefficient? For if they do not, then the above imagined structure of the normal fluid would be clearly illusory.

Landau, in his original paper, attempted to satisfy himself on this point by using a statistical argument which, however, appears to have elements of circularity in it. Some years later, Khalatnikov, using the Landau spectrum, was able to deduce a viscosity coefficient which is in reasonable accord with the experimental data (see Fig. 27).

measurements. The present values for the three are

$$\frac{\Delta}{k} = 9.6°K \qquad \mu = 0.77m \qquad \frac{p_0}{\hbar} = 2 \ A^{-1}$$

where m is the mass of the helium atom.

The Superfluid Component. The main problem now remaining is to account for the existence and properties of the superfluid phase, and among the latter the problem of the frictionless flow is clearly paramount.

At absolute zero the liquid will be all superfluid or, better said, in its ground state. Imagine this liquid to be flowing through, say, a capillary. In order for friction to manifest itself, there must be an energy dissipation either at the capillary wall or within the liquid itself; i.e., some rotons and/or phonons must be generated from the kinetic energy of the stream. Thus the latter would be diminished, the flow slowed down, and the "superfluidity" lost. The question arises, therefore, as to what velocity of flow would be needed to produce a roton or phonon.

Referring back to Fig. 43, we note that a straight line through the origin, plotted on this diagram, has a slope which represents velocity. In order to generate a roton, the minimum slope (velocity) required would be that of a line just tangent to the roton branch of the curve.[1] Now

$$E_{rot} = \frac{(p - p_0)^2}{2\mu} + \Delta$$

that is,
$$\frac{E_{rot}}{p} = \frac{(p - p_0)^2}{2\mu p} + \frac{\Delta}{p} \qquad (37)$$

---

[1] Landau's argument is substantially as follows. Consider a mass M of helium, at $0°K$, flowing through a horizontal pipe. If the velocity of flow, v, becomes large enough, we might guess that a roton (or phonon) is created at the expense of some kinetic energy from the stream.

If ε and p are the energy and momentum of a roton when the helium is at rest, then, to an observer stationed on the pipe, the energy of the system is

$$E = \tfrac{1}{2}Mv^2 \qquad v < v_{crit}$$
$$E = \varepsilon + \mathbf{p} \cdot \mathbf{v} + \tfrac{1}{2}Mv^2 \qquad v > v_{crit}$$

Since the excitation will tend to drag the pipe in the direction of the stream, the momentum p must be opposite to v. The quantity $(\varepsilon - pv)$ when $v > v_{crit}$ must be negative or else the energy of the system would increase by creating an excitation. Hence

$$\varepsilon - pv_{crit} < 0$$

that is,
$$v_{crit} > \frac{\varepsilon}{p}$$

Hence if we minimize expression (37), this will represent the minimum velocity the fluid must have to generate a roton—any lesser velocity will not do, and the helium will remain nondissipative, i.e., superfluid. We find that (37) is a minimum if $p^2 = p_0^2 + 2\mu\Delta$, which on resubstitution into (37) gives

$$\left(\frac{E_{\text{rot}}}{p}\right)_{\min} = \frac{1}{\mu}(\sqrt{p_0^2 + 2\mu\Delta} - p_0) \tag{38}$$

For $p_0 = 0$ (original Landau spectrum) this reduces to

$$\sqrt{\frac{2\Delta}{\mu}} \cong 80 \text{ m/sec} \tag{39}$$

For phonons, since this branch of the spectrum is itself a straight line, clearly

$$\left(\frac{E_{\text{ph}}}{p}\right)_{\min} = c \cong 240 \text{ m/sec} \tag{40}$$

We conclude, therefore, that if the helium flows with a velocity not greater than about 80 m/sec, no phonons or rotons can be formed and the stream will remain nondissipative or superfluid. Strictly speaking, of course, this is at absolute zero; at a higher temperature where there already exist some rotons and phonons the situation could be different. Expression (39) reveals an important fact; namely, if there were no assumed energy gap, $\Delta = 0$, the "critical" velocity would also be zero, which means that superfluid flow could never occur.

There is a body of experimental evidence which indicates that, above a certain critical velocity of flow, such flow does indeed lose its frictionless character. But the velocities observed are orders of magnitude less than 80 m/sec.[1] This vast discrepancy, which also occurs in later theories, remains one of the outstanding puzzles connected with He II.

Landau postulated yet another condition for the velocity of superfluid flow, namely,

$$\nabla \times \mathbf{v}_s = 0$$

In a classical viscous liquid, at and near a solid boundary, this condition is clearly not true, since the liquid will possess a velocity gradient perpendicular to this boundary.[2] Hence the above equation is rather

[1] They vary, in different experiments, all the way from $\frac{1}{10}$ cm/sec up to a maximum of around 70 cm/sec.

[2] This follows from Stokes' theorem:

$$\iint(\nabla \times \mathbf{v}) \cdot d\mathbf{S} = \oint \mathbf{v} \cdot d\mathbf{l}$$

where dl is a line element of the surface S.

what one might expect for a frictionless liquid.   On the other hand, it is necessary to make a distinction between zero viscosity and zero curl, since the former, according to the Navier-Stokes equation, would require only that the curl of the fluid velocity should be a constant, not necessarily zero.

We shall discuss this matter further along but, in the meantime, the zero curl condition, if true, probably derives from the quantum mechanics of the system.

A QUESTION OF STATISTICS

In Landau's theory the statistics of the atomic nuclei which form the He II are nowhere explicitly invoked.   But the alpha particle, possessing no nuclear spin, is known, via quantum mechanics, to obey Bose statistics.   On the other hand, the stable isotope He^3 does possess a spin of one half and hence would obey Fermi statistics.

It is true that we have assumed Bose statistics for the excitations, but this has nothing to do with the nuclear properties.   In other words, we should expect similar excitations in liquid He^3; i.e., according to Landau's ideas this liquid should also exhibit superfluidity with the expectation, of course, that the lambda point be different than for He II.

The experimental evidence to date concerning superfluidity in He^3 is not entirely satisfactory.   We can, however, say that He^3 has no lambda point above 1°K (its normal boiling point is 3.2°K) and *probably* none above about 0.1°K.   Further, there is fairly strong quantum-mechanical evidence that the existence of roton states in He II is a consequence of the symmetrical nature of the wave functions of individual helium atoms.

Prior to Landau's theory, F. London had approached the He II problem from a quite different point of view in which he invoked an earlier and forgotten calculation by Einstein concerning the properties of an ideal gas which obeyed Bose statistics.   In such an assembly, as the temperature is lowered, a point is reached wherein the particles begin to go into a highly degenerate ground state; this process is complete at absolute zero when all the atoms are in this state.   This behavior is highly reminiscent of a part of the two-fluid postulates.[1]

If we use numbers appropriate to helium gas, the transition temperature turns out to be 3.14°K, not too far removed from the actual lambda point in He II.   The derived specific heat of the gas shows a

---

[1] No mathematical details are given, since the subject is exhaustively treated in F. London's "Superfluids," vol. II.

discontinuity at the transition temperature which is reminiscent of, though different from, that occurring at the actual lambda transition in He II.

The fact that He³, although a "quantum liquid" in the sense that it remains a liquid at very low temperatures, does not show superfluidity emerges at once from the model due to the statistics.

It appears, therefore, that an "ultimate" theory of He II must embrace both the Landau and London viewpoints. And the question arises as to what we mean by an ultimate theory. The answer has to be that it must be based, as completely as possible, on the most fundamental principle in the whole of physics, namely, Schrödinger's equation.

FEYNMAN'S EXTENSION OF THE LANDAU THEORY

The most serious drawback to Landau's formulation derives from the fact that He³, experimentally, does not appear to be a superfluid even though it is undoubtedly a "quantum" liquid. By this latter we mean that liquid He³ remains a liquid, under saturated vapor pressure, down to absolute zero. Said differently, there is nothing in Landau's theory which would preclude superfluidity in He³—we should, in fact, expect it, although there is no way of predicting how low its lambda temperature ought to lie.

In order to achieve a more fundamental formulation than Landau's it would appear necessary to solve Schrödinger's equation for the aggregate of roughly 10^{22} particles, each interacting with one another, which constitute 1 cm³ of He II. But this is clearly a fantastic impossibility. Fortunately, as Feynman[1] has shown, we can still throw considerable light on the problem by making use of our intuitive knowledge of the general behavior of quantum-mechanical systems.

We know, for instance, that generally speaking a ground-state wave function has no nodes; but those representing excited states do have nodes as a consequence of the orthogonality requirement. Again when the gradient, or slope, of a given wave function is large, the energy of the state is generally high[2]—in other words, for excited states near the ground state the wave functions must have minimal gradients. Further, and this is most important to Feynman's argument, the wave

---

[1] R. P. Feynman, *Phys. Rev.*, **94**:262 (1954). This paper includes references to his previous work.

[2] The reader may refresh his memory by looking at the wave functions for the ground state and first few excited states of some simple system, say the harmonic oscillator or a particle in a potential well.

functions for a system obeying Bose statistics are symmetrical. Physically this means that the particles in such an aggregate are indistinguishable. Hence if a pair of particles simply exchange places, the wave function of the aggregate remains unchanged.

Now, as has been mentioned, helium differs from a classical liquid in that it remains liquid down to 0°K. In order to freeze it, we have to exert considerable pressure ($\sim$26 atm), i.e., force the atoms to occupy a smaller volume. In ordinary substances—for example, liquid hydrogen—the stable low-temperature phase is a solid; i.e., the minimum potential energy of the system occurs for this configuration. But in helium the situation is unusual on two counts. First, the attractive force between two helium atoms is unusually weak until they approach closely, when it becomes strong and repulsive. Second, the zero-point momentum, as a consequence of the small atomic mass, is large.[1] The net consequence is to keep the atoms far apart such that the weak attractive forces never succeed in pulling them together in the usual solid configuration. This is confirmed by the fact that the measured atomic volume of He II (the volume "owned" by each atom) is exceptionally large—about 46 A³. The ground-state wave function for the He II aggregate must reflect these facts and, in addition, possess no nodes.

The amplitude of this wave function, ϕ, must be a maximum at the above spacing; if the atoms, for any reason, approach more closely, ϕ must decrease, reflecting thereby a less probable configuration. For low excited states it seems reasonable that their wave functions should contain ϕ as a factor to bar configurations which would bring the atoms too close together, since these would be states of very high energy.

Now the wave function of any such excited state will be a very complicated, but definite, mathematical expression involving the coordinates of *all* the atoms in the aggregate. In general, if we change the position of any atom, we will change its coordinates and hence change the wave function of the system.

Our primary purpose, with the above discussion in mind, is to try to show that there can be no excited states whose energies lie below those of the phonons. If we fail in this, we shall have negated Landau's approach entirely. Now we are familiar with a phonon as a wave or density fluctuation in the fluid with particle-like properties. The

[1] This is a consequence of the uncertainty principle. If we try to confine the atoms spatially (in a liquid or solid), their momentum becomes large; and this, for a light atom, means a high vibrational frequency. Hence their kinetic energy at the absolute zero will be large, whereas classically it would be nil.

wave function must therefore look something like

$$\psi_{\mathrm{ph}} \sim e^{ikx}$$

For low-lying states, with minimal energy above the ground state, k (the wave number) must be small, since the expected value of the energy appropriate to this wave function is $\hbar^2 k^2/2m$. This means that such excitations must have a long wavelength. We note, also, that this wave function is incomplete for reasons previously given; i.e., we must multiply it by ϕ.

Now our compressional wave is only one of a large number of possibilities for changing the configuration of the atoms in the aggregate and hence altering the wave function and so producing a different excitation. We have to be sure that some different arrangement will not lead to even lower energies.

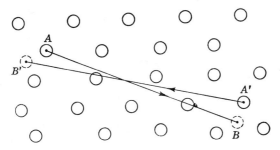

FIG. 45. Illustrating a change in configuration and hence in wave function by transporting atoms from A to B and from A' to B' over a long distance in an attempt to produce a gentle gradient of the wave function. (*Feynman*, 1953.)

This new assumed arrangement must, however, produce a wave function which is compelled, as we have seen, to meet the following conditions. It must be orthogonal to ψ_{ph} and ϕ; it must be symmetrical owing to Bose statistics; and it must have a small gradient (in configuration space) if it is to represent a low energy state. It is precisely these last two conditions which, as we shall see, rule out any possibility of excited states below, or even close to, the phonons.

In order to give this supposed wave function a gentle gradient, we must be able to create a new wave function by moving an atom a long way in configuration space. And we must be able to do this in such a way that no density fluctuations are created, for this would represent an unwanted phonon. To illustrate the situation, consider Fig. 45, which represents a certain configuration. Suppose we shift atom A a long distance (i.e., many atomic spacings) to B, a place not previously occupied. This would create a hole at A's original position and so produce an unwanted density fluctuation. To get around this, we move atom A' to position B', where B and B' are close to the initial configuration. All this has created a new configuration with an excited-state wave function of small gradient. But has it?

Because of the indistinguishability of the atoms, we could get exactly the same new wave function by merely moving A to B' and A' to B *over a much smaller distance*. Because of the statistics, therefore, we are forced into a steep gradient for our new (i.e., apart from phonons) wave function, and this means a high energy excitation. Whatever kind of motion we try—for instance, motion of atoms around a ring—we are forced to the same general conclusion. We conclude, therefore, that low-lying states (apart from phonons) cannot exist in He II. And the long-sought role of the Bose statistics, quite absent from Landau's formulation, emerges very naturally.

Our task now is to find the explicit form of the wave function for the higher energy states which we identify with Landau's rotons. If this can be done, it will then be possible to compute the expectation value of the energy, which expression may contain factors which can be measured experimentally. An independent check on Landau's roton spectrum would then be possible. Based on arguments given above plus the, so far, unused requirement that these roton wave functions must be orthogonal to that of the ground state, Feynman guesses that

$$\psi_{\text{rot}} = \sum_j f(r_j) \phi$$

where $f(r_j)$ is some function of the position r_j of the jth atom, the sum being taken over all the atoms. As is well known, ψ_{rot} will then be a solution of Schrödinger's equation when the energy integral $\int \psi_{\text{rot}}^* H \psi_{\text{rot}} \, d\tau$ is stationary, provided ψ_{rot} is normalized. This variational procedure determines the unknown function $f(r_j)$ to be $e^{i(\mathbf{k} \cdot \mathbf{r}_j)}$ and so

$$\psi_{\text{rot}} = \sum_j e^{i(\mathbf{k} \cdot \mathbf{r}_j)} \phi$$

This is somewhat surprising since it has the same form as that for phonons, and we should guess offhand that it would be quite different. However, it must be remembered that the latter are restricted to the smallest values of k. It is readily demonstrated that this wave function is, as needed, orthogonal to ϕ provided we exclude $k = 0$. Obviously, the above wave function is an exceedingly crude approximation, but the proof of the pudding will come if we can obtain anything like the roton energy spectrum out of it.

The standard procedure to find energies is to make use of the relation

$$E = \frac{\int \psi^* H \psi \, d\tau}{\int \psi^* \psi \, d\tau}$$

where H is the Hamiltonian operator and $d\tau$ is an element of volume in the configuration space defined by the coordinates of all the atoms. Feynman evaluates this expression as

$$E = \frac{\hbar^2 k^2}{2m S(k)}$$

where

$$S(k) = \int p(r) e^{i(\mathbf{k} \cdot \mathbf{r})} \, d^3 r$$

Thus if we can determine $S(k)$, we will have the energy of the excitations as a function of k or, as we hope, the Landau spectrum. But in order to understand the meaning of the symbols in $S(k)$, we will have to digress a bit.

In any liquid, over a distance of some few atomic diameters, there is some degree of regularity. This we know as a result of X-ray studies of the liquid state. This regularity is evidenced as a grouping of several atoms at some fairly well-defined distance about an arbitrarily selected atom. The group, or "shell," may be followed by a second shell at some larger distance, and, generally speaking, this ordering does not persist beyond a very few such shells. Hence the X-ray diffraction pattern of a liquid consists of one or two diffuse rings only vaguely reminiscent of the series of sharp lines we obtain in a solid, indicative nonetheless of some degree of order.

The quantity $S(k)$ reflects these facts and in X-ray analysis is commonly called the "structure factor." In it $p(r_1 - r_2) \, d^3 r$ is the probability of finding an atom at r_2 if one is known to be at r_1 ($d^3 r$ represents an element of volume in the ordinary space occupied by the liquid). Since two atoms may not overlap, $p(r)$ must be something like a δ function at the origin.

The actual determination of $S(k)$ involves a somewhat complicated mixture of experiment and theory and has been determined for He II by Beaumont and Reekie.[1] The experiment consists in measuring the intensity of the scattered X radiation, from a monochromatic source ($\lambda = 1.54$ A), as a function of the angle between the scattered X ray and the incident beam. For helium, where the large zero-point motion makes the rings especially diffuse, the experiment is especially difficult and subject to numerous corrections. Nevertheless, $S(k)$ is probably reliably known to within 10 per cent.

In any event, the result when fed into Feynman's formula shows an

[1] C. F. Beaumont and J. Reekie, *Proc. Roy. Soc.*, **A228**:363 (1955).

$E(k)$ versus k curve similar to Landau's with a minimum in the energy at about the right value of k. The gap Δ, however, turns out to be about twice that found by Landau from the calorimetric data. Nevertheless, the Landau spectrum has indeed been produced from "first principles."

If we consider an elementary excitation near the minimum roton spectrum, its energy in terms of wave vector k is

$$\varepsilon = \Delta + \frac{\hbar^2(k - k_0)^2}{2\mu}$$

The momentum of the excitation is $p = \hbar k$ and its group velocity is

$$v_g = \frac{1}{\hbar}\frac{\partial \varepsilon}{\partial k} = \frac{\hbar(k - k_0)}{\mu}$$

Hence for the lowest possible roton energy, when $k = k_0$, we have

$$v_g = 0$$
$$p = \hbar k_0 \neq 0$$

This result, from the point of view of classical particle dynamics, would indeed be paradoxical, but it must be remembered that a roton is composed of several helium atoms—not just one.

Thus we might imagine a roton to be a small circular vortex analogous to a smoke ring. It is true that such a classical vortex will move through the fluid with a definite drift velocity, but this arises because the ring tends to shrink in radius in order to reduce its energy. In the case of our roton above, it can shrink no further since it is clearly in its ground state. Hence its drift velocity is zero.

The phonon, on the other hand, behaves more like a classical particle since its energy is $\hbar k c$, and its group velocity is therefore c, the velocity of first sound.

All this means that the wave functions of the two excitations cannot possibly have the same form as the above analysis seems to show, and it turns out that this error is the principal reason why the calculated energy gap Δ is more than twice the experimental value. Later Feynman constructed a new wave function for the roton which brings the two values into much better agreement.

DETERMINATION OF THE LANDAU SPECTRUM BY NEUTRON-SCATTERING EXPERIMENTS

In 1957 Cohen and Feynman[1] proposed an interesting method in which the shape of the Landau spectrum for the normal component

[1] M. Cohen and R. P. Feynman, *Phys. Rev.*, **107**:13 (1957).

of the He II could be directly measured by observing the scattering of monoenergetic neutrons. In its simplest aspect, a neutron (momentum p_i) collides elastically with a roton (or phonon) and is thereby scattered through an angle φ as measured from its incident direction, acquiring a new momentum p_f. The roton, initially at rest, thereby acquires an energy E and a momentum p. In view of the conservation of energy and momentum in the collision process we can, accordingly, write

$$E = \frac{p_i^2}{2m} - \frac{p_f^2}{2m}$$
$$p^2 = p_i^2 + p_f^2 - 2p_i p_f \cos \varphi$$

If, therefore, we are able to measure p_i and p_f as well as φ, we can determine E and p. Thus if p_i is varied—or alternatively φ—we can trace out the E versus p curve or, in other words, the Landau spectrum.

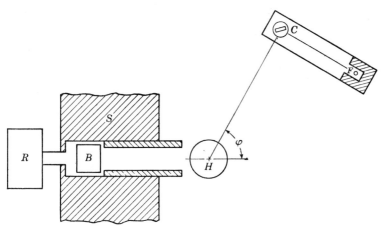

FIG. 46. Schematic of setup for neutron scattering experiments. R, reactor core; S, shielding; B, beryllium filter; H, helium, cryostat; C, NaCl crystal; F, $B^{10}F_3$ counter. (*Yarnell*, 1959.)

Cohen and Feynman further show that if we employ slow neutrons ($\lambda_i \approx 4$ A) and low temperatures for the liquid ($T < 2.2°$K), processes apart from the above, such as the production (or annihilation) of multiple excitations, are likely to occur at a negligible rate.

The first experimentalists to test these ideas were Palevsky et al.[1] in 1957. Nearly simultaneously, other groups of investigators did very similar work, and we will discuss that of Yarnell et al.[2] as being very complete and convincing.

[1] Palevsky, Otnes, Larsson, Pauli, and Stedman, *Phys. Rev.*, **108**:1346 (1957).
[2] Yarnell, Arnold, Bendt, and Kerr, *Phys. Rev.*, **113**:1379 (1959).

Obviously, the first requirement for a successful trial is a copious source of neutrons, i.e., a reactor. The above authors used one of the Los Alamos reactors producing a usable flux of 4×10^{12} neutrons/cm^2 sec. However, the neutrons from any thermal reactor are far from monochromatic—they possess a Maxwellian distribution (i.e., a continuous-wavelength distribution) corresponding to the moderator temperature which is above 300°K. Hence to obtain the "cold" monoenergetic beam which the proposed experiment requires, some sort of velocity selector or filter is necessary. The procedure, in all the

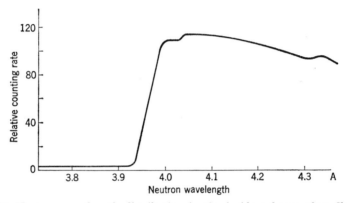

FIG. 47. Neutron wavelength distribution in the incident beam after filtering. (*Yarnell*, 1959.)

experiments, is to make use of the wave properties of neutrons and cause them to undergo Bragg reflection in a crystal.[1] The crystal material, of course, must be such that it does not appreciably absorb or incoherently scatter the neutrons; beryllium is suitable in this respect. If we place a piece of polycrystalline beryllium in the neutron beam, all neutrons whose wavelength is less than twice the maximum spacing between planes in the crystal lattice will be greatly attenuated. At the same time all particles having a longer wavelength than this will emerge with but slightly diminished velocities. Hence a sharp discontinuity in the neutron velocity (i.e., longer wavelength) distribution will occur. Thus if neutrons with such a velocity distribution are scattered from He II at a fixed angle φ, then, according to the theoretical prediction above, the velocity distribution of the scattered neutrons should also exhibit this sharp edge, but at a longer wavelength. This clever device, therefore, gives us what amounts to monochromatic neutrons at large intensity. Figure 47 illustrates this effect.

[1] This is preferable to using a monochromator such as a "time-of-flight" chopper, since the beam intensity in such a device is too low.

In order to measure the wavelength and hence the momentum
($p = h/\lambda$) of the incident and scattered neutrons, these investigators
employed a crystal spectrometer using a natural crystal of NaCl in
much the same way as it is employed in the classical determination of
X-ray wavelengths using a known crystal lattice. The neutron

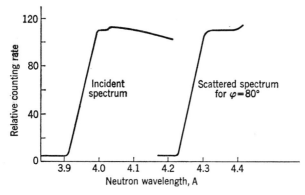

FIG. 48. Relative neutron intensity versus wavelength for the incident and scattered beam. Background intensity subtracted. $T = 1.1°K$. (*Yarnell*, 1959.)

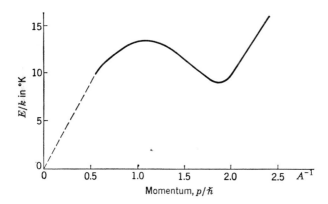

FIG. 49. The Landau spectrum experimentally measured. Temperature 1.1°K.
(*Yarnell*, 1959.)

detectors used with the spectrometer consisted of gas-filled counters
using $B^{10}F_3$. In addition, the beam from the pile was monitored by
use of a U^{235} fission counter. A very schematic view of the setup is
shown in Fig. 46. The experiment is a highly sophisticated one from
the cryogenics point of view, requiring quite special all-metal Dewars.

Figure 48 shows a typical run at about 1.1°K at $\varphi = 80°$. Figure 49

shows the deduced Landau spectrum for He II at 1.1°K.   It is interesting to compare the parameters Δ/k, $p_0/\hbar$, and μ as deduced from these
measurements with those obtained by Landau from the calorimetric
data; the following table shows the comparison.

	Calorimetric data	Neutron scattering
Δ/k..........	9.6°K	8.65° K
$p_0/\hbar$.........	2.0 A^{-1}	1.92 A^{-1}
μ............	0.77 m$_{He}$	0.16 m$_{He}$

The agreement is seen to be very good with the exception of the roton
mass.   Further, the slope of the dotted line in Fig. 49 comes out to be
239 ± 5 m/sec[1] in excellent accord with what we know of the first
sound velocity near absolute zero.   Finally, experiments on the position and shape of the minimum in the Landau spectrum at 1.6 and
1.8°K showed very little deviation from that at 1.1°K, which is certainly a most satisfying result.

[1] As does also the slope of the straight portion of the curve for momenta higher
than p_0.

CHAPTER 6

Helium in Rotation

SOME CLASSICAL CONSIDERATIONS

Mention has previously been made of Landau's postulate concerning the curl of the superfluid velocity field, viz., curl $\mathbf{v}_s = 0$. This postulate, if true, leads to some interesting consequences since it is radically different from that which governs the behavior of an ordinary viscous liquid.

Consider a classical liquid contained in a cylindrical vessel of radius a and let the latter be set in rotation about its vertical axis of symmetry at a small angular velocity ω. We are interested in the steady-state ($\partial v / \partial t = 0$) rotation of the liquid. To good approximation we may treat the problem two-dimensionally, being required to find $v_\theta = f(r)$ where v_θ is the tangential velocity of the fluid at distance r from the axis of rotation. Since we postulate the velocities as small, we may ignore terms involving v^2 such as $(\mathbf{v} \cdot \nabla)\mathbf{v}$ or ∇p. The Navier-Stokes equation,

$$\rho \frac{\partial \mathbf{v}}{\partial t} + \rho(\mathbf{v} \cdot \nabla)\mathbf{v} = -\nabla p + \eta \nabla^2 \mathbf{v}$$

then reads
$$\nabla^2 \mathbf{v} = 0 \tag{1}$$

The boundary conditions are
$$v_r = 0$$
$$\frac{\partial v_\theta}{\partial \theta} = 0$$

The last one is a consequence of the incompressibility, i.e., $\nabla \cdot \mathbf{v} = 0$.

If we call the unit vectors in the r and θ directions, respectively, $\hat{r}$ and $\hat{\theta}$ such that

$$\mathbf{v} = \hat{r}v_r + \hat{\theta}v_\theta$$

then Eq. (1) in these coordinates becomes

$$\nabla^2\mathbf{v} = \hat{r}\left(\nabla^2 v_r - \frac{v_r}{r^2} - \frac{2}{r^2}\frac{\partial v_\theta}{\partial\theta}\right) + \hat{\theta}\left(\nabla^2 v_\theta - \frac{v_\theta}{r^2} + \frac{2}{r^2}\frac{\partial v_r}{\partial\theta}\right)$$

which, in view of the boundary conditions, gives

$$\nabla^2\mathbf{v} = \hat{\theta}\left(\nabla^2 v_\theta - \frac{v_\theta}{r^2}\right)$$

But
$$\nabla^2 v_\theta = \frac{1}{r}\frac{\partial}{\partial r}\left(r\frac{\partial v_\theta}{\partial r}\right) + \frac{1}{r^2}\frac{\partial^2 v_\theta}{\partial\theta^2}$$

$$= \frac{1}{r}\frac{\partial}{\partial r}\left(r\frac{\partial v_\theta}{\partial r}\right)$$

Hence
$$\nabla^2\mathbf{v} = \hat{\theta}\left[\frac{1}{r}\frac{\partial}{\partial r}\left(r\frac{\partial v_\theta}{\partial r}\right) - \frac{v_\theta}{r^2}\right] = 0$$

that is,
$$r\frac{d^2 v_\theta}{dr^2} + \frac{dv_\theta}{dr} - \frac{v_\theta}{r} = 0 \tag{2}$$

Now $v_\theta = r\omega$ satisfies Eq. (2), as may readily be checked by direct substitution, and also satisfies the boundary condition that $v_\theta = a\omega$ when $r = a$, a basic requirement for a viscous fluid. But this velocity field is precisely that for the liquid rotating as a solid body. We note, in passing, that curl $v_\theta = 2\omega$ for this motion.[1]

Solid-body motion is not the only type of field which will satisfy Eq. (2). For instance, and again by direct substitution, the field $v_\theta = a^2\omega/r$ satisfies both (2) and the boundary condition at the wall of the containing vessel. This field is that of a vortex with a hollow core (radius b) along the axis of rotation. The reader may satisfy himself

[1] For our two-dimensional motion, wherein $v = f(r)$ only, we have by Stokes' theorem

$$\oint \mathbf{v} \cdot d\mathbf{l} = \iint \text{curl } \mathbf{v} \cdot d\mathbf{S}$$

that is,
$$2\pi r v = 2\pi \int (r \text{ curl } v)\, dr$$

whence, differentiating,

$$\text{Curl } v = \frac{1}{r}\frac{d}{dr}(rv)$$

It follows at once that

$$v = r\omega \qquad \text{curl } v = 2\omega$$
$$v = \frac{A}{r} \qquad \text{curl } v = 0$$

readily that for this particular velocity distribution the curl $v_\theta = 0$, $r > b$.

It is of interest to compare the energies associated with these two modes, which are clearly given by $\pi\rho\int v_\theta^2 r\, dr$. Thus we have

$$\mathcal{E}_{\text{solid}} = \pi\rho \int_0^a \omega^2 r^3\, dr = \frac{\pi\rho a^4 \omega^2}{4} \tag{3}$$

$$\mathcal{E}_{\text{vortex}} = \pi\rho \int_b^a \frac{a^4\omega^2}{r^2} r\, dr = \pi\rho a^4\omega^2 \ln \frac{a}{b} \tag{4}$$

These two energies become equal when

$$\ln \frac{a}{b} = \frac{1}{4}$$

that is,
$$b \cong 0.8a$$

This is very much larger than we should expect the core of the vortex to be, and so we guess that the solid-body configuration will have the lower energy and will, therefore, be the preferred one. We may sum up the situation by stating that in the classical viscous liquid the motion is such that the curl of the fluid velocity will never vanish.[1]

OSBORNE'S EXPERIMENT

The Landau criterion $\nabla \times \mathbf{v}_s = 0$, in a simply connected region, requires that $v_s = 0$ provided there is no motion perpendicular to the boundary.[2] On the other hand, in the classical liquid $\nabla \times \mathbf{v} = 2\omega$, which leads to a free surface which is, as we know, parabolic in shape. The Landau postulate, therefore, leads us to the conclusion that, in an experiment of the above type, the fluid motion will be quite different than in the case of a classical liquid. The first experimentalist to realize this was D. V. Osborne who, in 1950[3], tried rotating He II in such a cylindrical vessel. In order to detect differences in the fluid motion between helium and the classical liquid, he measured the shape of the free surface as a function of ω at several different temperatures in the He II region.

[1] By a variational analysis whereby the energy is minimized under the constraint that the angular momentum remain constant, it turns out that the resulting velocity field is indeed solid-body type.

[2] This follows from Stokes' theorem, which is valid only for a simply connected region. Thus

$$\int\int (\nabla \times \mathbf{v}_s) \cdot d\mathbf{S} = \oint \mathbf{v}_s \cdot d\mathbf{l}$$

wherein dl is a line element bounding the area S.

[3] D. V. Osborne, *Proc. Phys. Soc. (London)*, **63**:909 (1950).

According to the above, therefore, we should expect that if we rotate He II at absolute zero, the free surface will be a straight line apart from small surface tension effects. At higher temperatures, of course, when the normal classical component comes into play, the shape should be something intermediate between this and a parabola. The point is that the shape of the free surface ought to be temperature dependent in the available He II region.

Osborne's results, however, turned out to be negative. Within the experimental error the surface was a classical parabola at all speeds and temperatures. We will postpone further discussion of this interesting experiment until later.

OTHER EARLY ROTATION EXPERIMENTS

About the time that Osborne was doing his experiment a very similar one was performed independently by Andronikashvili and Kaverkin. The result was the same except that, on occasion and at sufficiently high speeds, they observed a vortex formation in the rotating beaker.

In addition, in 1952 Andronikashvili performed an interesting experiment making use of his pile-of-discs technique.[1] The purpose of the experiment was to look for a "persistent current" in He II. He used a pile of discs suspended by the usual torsion fiber and mirror system and closely surrounded by a stationary metal can filled with liquid helium. By means of a magnet-eddy current arrangement the system could be braked at will.

The disc system was brought into steady rotation (by means of a small motor driving the torsion fiber) at 30 rpm at a temperature just below the λ point. The following procedure was then applied:

1. Still rotating, the helium was cooled to 1.5°K.
2. At this temperature the system was brought to rest (in 15 sec).
3. The brake was then removed and the helium warmed to 1.65°K (again in 15 sec).

The idea of the experiment was as follows. Since, near the λ point, practically all the fluid was normal, it was all brought into rotation at 30 rpm. In step 1 a certain fraction of the fluid became superfluid (without viscosity), and this portion remained rotating. In step 2 the normal fraction was arrested because of the stopping of the discs. The superfluid fraction ignored this, however. In step 3 some part of this presumably still rotating superfluid was reconverted back to normal fluid again ($\rho_n/\rho = 0.12$ at 1.5°K, $\rho_n/\rho = 0.22$ at 1.65°K). Because of its viscosity, this should exert a momentary torque on the

[1] E. L. Andronikashvili, *J. Exptl. Theoret. Phys. (U.S.S.R.)*, **22**:62 (1952).

stationary (but free-to-move) disc system, resulting in an observable ballistic deflection.

By conservation of angular momentum,

$$\dot{i}\omega = (I + \dot{i})\Omega \cong I\Omega$$

where $\dot{i}$ = moment of inertia of superfluid which is "destroyed"

ω = 30 rpm

I = moment of inertia of disc system

Ω = initial angular velocity of disc system

Further, $\frac{1}{2}I\Omega^2 = \frac{1}{2}k\varphi^2$

where k is the torsion-fiber constant and φ is the observed ballistic deflection. Hence φ is determinable. From the parameters of the experiment, φ computes as 27°.

Actually φ's of only 1 to 2° were observed which, moreover, did not depend on the prior direction of ω. Hence the experiment turned out negative. The usual explanation given for the negative result is that the speed ω was far too high. In the light of later work this explanation appears dubious.

It would appear, therefore, that the early rotation experiments were all bedeviled in that they produced negative results. There is, however, one early experiment—actually the earliest—which turned out positive, albeit this was probably fortuitous. This experiment was reported in 1941 by P. L. Kapitza.[1] A vertical glass capillary was provided with a coaxial glass rod such that there was a narrow annular gap for the helium. Arrangements were made such that the glass rod could be rotated at various angular velocities. Kapitza measured the thermal conductivity of the liquid helium II in the annular space, by usual resistance-thermometry techniques, as a function of the rotational speed of the central rod. The result indicated that there was a decrease in the thermal conduction of He II under rotation as compared with the system at rest. As mentioned, the result was probably fortuitous—rather similar measurements performed with better sensitivity at Yale were negative, for example. Nevertheless, it contained the germ of an idea which, as we shall see, led to the first successful (i.e., definitely positive) rotation experiment.

SECOND SOUND AND ROTATION

Wheeler, Blakewood, and Lane[2] decided to resurrect Kapitza's experiment, casting it, however, in a more modern guise. Accepting

[1] P. L. Kapitza, *J. Phys.* (*U.S.S.R.*), **4**:181 (1941).

[2] Wheeler, Blakewood, and Lane, *Phys. Rev.*, **99**:1667 (1955).

the Kapitza results at face value, these authors felt that the properties of the superfluid seemed to be radically modified by rotation. They accordingly decided to use a uniquely superfluid phenomenon—the second sound—as the test vehicle as opposed to the thermal conductivity, which is not exclusively a superfluid effect.

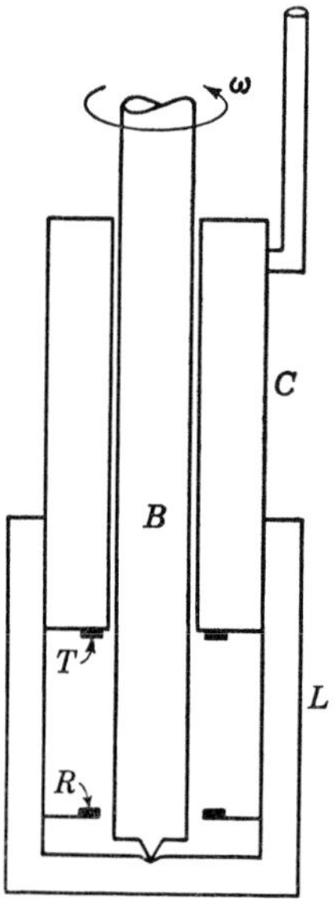

With this in mind, they employed an apparatus (Fig. 50) essentially very similar to Kapitza's. The helium was contained in an annular space between concentric cylinders; the inner cylinder (B) was capable of various speeds of rotation, while the outer (L) remained fixed. T and R were two carbon resistance thermometers in the form of thin annular strips. They could be used as either second sound generators or detectors. The length of the annular cavity could be varied by raising or lowering the plunger C from outside the cryostat. The electronics consisted of the usual time-of-flight square-pulse technique. In this way both the second sound velocity and the height and shape of the received pulses could be measured.

FIG. 50. Schematic of apparatus for measuring second sound attenuation caused by He II in rotation. (*Wheeler, Blakewood, and Lane*, 1955.)

The experiment, when tried, very quickly yielded the result that the second sound velocity was quite independent of the rotation of cylinder B. Specifically, when B was at rest this velocity did not differ by as much as $\frac{1}{10}$ per cent, as against the case when B had a speed of as much as 30 rps.

The situation regarding the attenuation of the pulses was, however, very different. It was observed that the attenuation of the thermal pulses was greatly increased when the liquid was set in rotation. This is illustrated in Fig. 51, wherein the ratio of the received pulse height at speed ω to that observed when $\omega = 0$ is plotted semilogarithmically against the length of the cavity. As is seen, this gives an exponential dependence on path length which is typical of an attenuation. As has been mentioned previously, the "natural" attenuation in He II is very small so that, on the scale of the plot, the curve for $\omega = 0$ would be indistinguishable from a line parallel to the horizontal axis of coordinates. The extra rotational attenuation is, therefore, very large. The explanation given by the authors for their effect had to do with the scattering of the elementary excitations by some sort of turbulence (i.e., vorticity) in the superfluid.   In the light of our present knowledge, this explanation is undoubtedly the correct one.

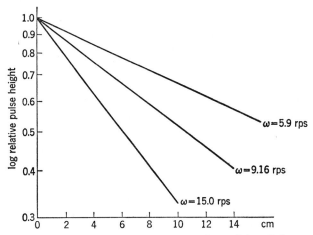

FIG. 51. The log of the relative pulse height versus the path length for second sound at 1.39°K.   By relative pulse height is meant the ratio of the amplitudes of the received second sound pulse at speed ω to the same when $\omega = 0$.   (*Wheeler, Blakewood, and Lane*, 1955.)

About the same time that this experiment was in progress, Hall and Vinen were, quite independently, carrying out an experiment which, at least superficially, was very similar.   Their interpretation was, however, along very different lines.   In fact, the experiment was based on some deliberations due to Onsager and hence, before discussing it, it is expedient to make a digression.

QUANTIZED VORTICES

Somewhat prior to 1950, L. Onsager made a notable contribution to the theory of superfluid helium.   Guided by very general quantum-mechanical arguments, he showed that a possible wave function for the liquid would lead to a motion analogous to classical vortex motion.   This, in turn, leads to a circulation composed of units of amount h/m, where m is the mass of the He atom.[1]   Feynman later

---

[1] The physical arguments behind this approach may be made clearer by the following example.   Consider a batch of superfluid to be moving with uniform translational velocity v.   The wave function of the system will then look something like

$$\psi = \Phi e^{ik\Sigma r_j}$$

where Φ is the ground-state wave function, r_j the position vector of any given came to exactly the same conclusion as an extension of his previously discussed studies of liquid helium.

At this point it is useful to recall some points connected with vortex theory in classical hydrodynamics. Here a common type of vortex consists of a central "core" (radius a) in which the fluid rotates as a solid body with, say, angular velocity ω. The curl of the fluid velocity is accordingly constant throughout the core and of magnitude 2ω. Surrounding the core the fluid velocity is of different form; namely, it is inversely proportional to r, the distance from the center of the core. Thus for $r > a$ the curl vanishes; i.e., the motion beyond the core is irrotational. If we apply Stokes' theorem to such a vortex model, we obtain the following results:

$$2\omega\pi r^2 = \oint v_i r\, d\theta \qquad r < a \qquad\qquad (5)$$
$$2\omega\pi a^2 = \oint v_o r\, d\theta \qquad r > a \qquad\qquad (6)$$

wherein v_i and v_o are the fluid velocities inside and outside the core, respectively. Since, by symmetry, neither of these is dependent on θ, the above gives

$$v_i = r\omega \qquad r < a \qquad\qquad (7)$$
$$v_o = \frac{\omega a^2}{r} \qquad r > a \qquad\qquad (8)$$

Also, Eq. (6) shows that the circulation outside the core is a constant, namely,

$$k_o = 2\pi\omega a^2 \qquad\qquad (9)$$

This, then, is the classical analogue of Onsager's unit vortex where, as we saw, the circulation is also constant of an amount $h/m \cong 10^{-3}$ cm^2/sec. In classical hydrodynamics the quantity $k_o/2\pi$ is called the "strength" of the vortex; accordingly, the quantum of vorticity has a

---

atom, and

$$k = \frac{p}{\hbar} = \frac{mv}{\hbar}$$

Consider next a chain of atoms in a ring and let each atom be displaced so that it occupies a position formerly occupied by its nearest neighbor. Because of the symmetrical properties of the Bose statistics, this operation will not change the wave function. The phase term in the wave function will, however, change by

$$\frac{m}{\hbar}\sum v\,\Delta r_j \cong \frac{m}{\hbar}\oint v\,dl$$

This quantity must, therefore, be either zero or $2\pi n$, where n is an integer. Hence

$$\oint v\,dl = n\frac{h}{m}$$

strength of $\hbar/m$. In the classical case it is simple to compute the pressure within the core (and outside) in terms of the pressure where the velocity field is sensibly zero. It then turns out that the pressure may be zero up to and including the distance $r = a$; i.e., the core may be hollow. A familiar case of this is provided by water emptying from a wash basin. If we shrink the core to infinitesimal dimensions in such a way that we preserve the strength of the vortex (as defined above) constant, we obtain what is called a vortex line or filament.

If instead of a single line we have an array of lines of equal strength, then, again applying Stoke's theorem, we may readily compute the circulation around any closed curve surrounding them.

Thus,

$$\iint (\nabla \times \mathbf{v}) \cdot d\mathbf{S} = N2\omega\pi a^2 = \oint \mathbf{v} \cdot d\mathbf{l}$$

that is,
$$Nk_o = \oint \mathbf{v} \cdot d\mathbf{l} \qquad (10)$$

where N is the number of enclosed lines.

In summary, therefore, we have the important result that, uniquely in superfluid helium, we may possess quantized vortices; or, said differently, there is a lower limit to the amount of circulation which may be induced in this fluid. It must be emphasized that these elementary vortices occur in the superfluid component only; the normal fluid has nothing to do with it. At first sight it might be supposed that these vortices form an additional excitation to the phonons and rotons. Calculation shows, however, that this is not so, since their statistical weight ($e^{-\varepsilon/kT}$) is virtually zero.

Potent as these ideas are, they nevertheless leave us with embarrassingly little information about the nature of these vortices, apart from their strength. We do not, for instance, have any real information about the core radius, apart from the fact that it must be hollow since we must continually bear in mind that liquid helium is not a classical continuum. We may, with Feynman, guess that it is very small—of the order of a few angstroms—but we must recognize that this is just a guess. For the same reason we can do no more than make extremely rough estimates of the kinetic energy (per unit length) of our lines. On the other hand, we can confidently carry over some of the well-established results of classical vortex theory into the new situation. Thus the Onsager vortices cannot terminate within the body of the fluid—they must end either at the free surface or else on the solid boundaries. A vortex wholly within the liquid must terminate "on itself," i.e., be a continuous curve like the familiar smoke ring. Also, classically, a vortex filament moves with the fluid in such a way that its strength remains constant. This means if the fluid moves, the line moves with it.

In addition to the above, there is a somewhat obscure theorem in classical hydrodynamics which has been much applied in the problem of rotating helium. If a cylinder, initially at rest in a fluid, has a circulation K around it (the axis of K and the cylinder being coincident) and a force f (per unit length) is applied normal to this axis, then the cylinder acquires a velocity u, with respect to the fluid, given by

$$\mathbf{f} = \rho(\mathbf{u} \times \mathbf{K})$$

where ρ is the fluid density. Thus f, u, and K are mutually perpendicular. Conversely, if the fluid possesses a velocity u with respect to the cylinder, then a lateral force f will act upon it. This is known, in the German literature, as the Magnus effect and is related to that of Bernoulli. The Magnus effect was used some years ago in Germany in the design of a unique sailing vessel. In place of sails the boat possessed a pair of vertical motor-driven cylinders. In the viscous air the rotating cylinders produced the necessary circulation, and the wind did the rest.

HALL AND VINEN'S EXPERIMENT

The first experimental evidence tending to support the vortex-line picture was reported by Hall and Vinen in 1956.[1] In principle, they measured the attenuation of the second sound in He II contained in a steadily rotating vessel under the following two conditions:

1. When the second sound was propagated parallel to the axis of rotation
2. When the second sound was propagated at right angles to this axis, i.e., radially

To measure the attenuation, they used a resonance technique wherein a constant signal at resonant frequency is fed into a resonator; an increase in attenuation is then observed as a decrease in the resonant amplitude of the second sound. Figure 52 illustrates, very schematically, the two types of resonant cavities used in the experiment. In both, the usual heater–resistance thermometer combination is employed, and the whole assembly, including the containing can, is made to rotate. The requisite electric leads enter the cryostat via mercury trough slip rings. The heater is fed with known-frequency alternating current, and the thermometer output after amplification and rectification is displayed on a galvanometer or a cathode-ray

[1] H. E. Hall and W. F. Vinen, *Proc. Roy. Soc.* (*London*), **A238**:204 (1956).

oscilloscope (C.R.O.). Since the input frequency is known and variable, resonance curves may be plotted from the galvanometer readings;
the whole procedure is exactly analogous to that employed to find the
Q values of microwave cavity resonators.

The results of experiments 1 and 2 showed that a large attenuation
due to rotation (comparable to that found by Wheeler, Blakewood,
and Lane) was observed for experiment 2. On the other hand, the
corresponding attenuation for case 1 was much less—of the order of
one-fifth that in case 2.

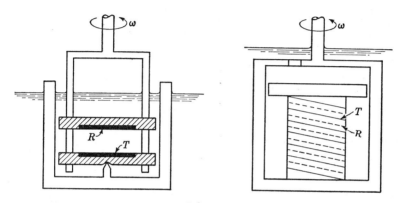

FIG. 52.

Left: Schematic of axial mode resonator. The heater T is a 60-cm length of
Eureka alloy wire wound as a pancake coil. The receiver R is similarly shaped,
but is made of 3-mil phosphor bronze. Note that both T and R rotate. (*Hall
and Vinen,* 1956.)

Right: Schematic of radial mode resonator. Both heater and receiver (T and R)
are wound on the central cylinder, and both T and R rotate. Maximum speed
employed was around 1 rps. (*Hall and Vinen,* 1956.)

Hall and Vinen considered this strong evidence for the existence of
vortex lines parallel to the axis of rotation. In other words, the
normal component—mainly rotons at the temperatures employed—
suffered energy loss by collision with the lines when propagated radially; the "collision cross section" of the lines in the other orientation
was, of course, much less. Hall and Vinen bolstered their argument
by considerable theoretical calculation, including an attempt to compute the equivalent diameter for a roton-vortex line collision. These
calculations are rendered most difficult by the fact that He II cannot
be treated as a continuum on the scale of the vortex line and also, of
course, by the previously mentioned fact that the structure of the line
is so uncertain.

THE ANGULAR MOMENTUM

The existence of quantized vortex lines places the whole question concerning the rotation of the superfluid in a cylindrical vessel (Osborne's experiment) in a new light, requiring, perhaps, a quite new approach.

We now wish to consider the following problem. Pure superfluid, in a cylindrical vessel, is rotating with a steady angular velocity Ω about the latter's axis of symmetry. We suppose also that the fluid is incompressible, which is a quite fair assumption for liquid helium.

Onsager and Feynman would visualize the liquid as containing a dense array of unit vortex lines (circulation of each h/m), each parallel to the rotational axis with their ends at, respectively, the bottom of the container and the free surface. The question now arises as to what kind of macroscopic velocity field the above array will produce.

At first sight this looks like a fairly involved computation, but we can arrive at a very reasonable estimate by making use of the known properties of the circulation around a vortex line. We recall that, outside the core of the line, the microscopic flow is irrotational, being $\hbar/mx$ where x is the distance from the center. It follows from Stokes' theorem that the circulation is the same around any contour outside of and surrounding the core. Further, the symmetry of the situation permits us to treat the problem two-dimensionally, and the incompressibility of the fluid requires that the macroscopic velocity field be independent of azimuth θ and dependent on r only.

Referring to Fig. 53, consider the elemental area between r and $(r + dr)$. Let there be a uniform array of vortices, each of constant circulation h/m and with the flow pattern as indicated. The velocity field of adjacent vortices will cancel out except at the boundaries r and $(r + dr)$. Suppose also we have a density of vortices of $n(r)$ lines/cm². Then the circulation around the boundaries will equal the sum of the circulations of the individual vortices. Thus, starting at A and proceeding round the contour as indicated by the arrows, we have

$$\left(v + \frac{dv}{dr}\,dr\right)2\pi(r + dr) - 2\pi rv = 2\pi r\,dr\,n(r)\frac{h}{m}$$

that is,
$$\frac{d}{dr}(rv) = rn(r)\frac{h}{m}$$

wherein $v = f(r)$ is the required velocity field at a distance r from the axis of rotation. As we have mentioned, the line density $n(r)$ is an arbitrary function of r but is independent of θ.

Consider now the special case where $n(r)$ is a constant, equal to, say, A. The last equation gives us immediately that $v = (Ah/2m)r$. This type of velocity field is a very familiar one, being that found in a solid body rotating with constant angular velocity $Ah/2m$. It is also, as we have seen, the preferred type of motion for a classical viscous fluid.

The above velocity field is based on the assumption of a spatially uniform line density for the elementary vortices, and it is now necessary to inquire whether this assumption is at all reasonable from the

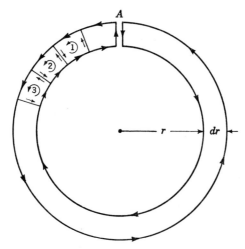

FIG. 53. Procedure used in calculating the macroscopic velocity field produced by an array of line vortices.

energy point of view; that is, whether the above type of array would lead to a minimum in the energy of the system, for if it would not, then it would be most unlikely to occur in practice.

To investigate this point, we shall first of all assume that the macroscopic velocity field is an arbitrary but well-behaved function of the radius vector r, say $v(r)$. Then the energy of the rotating fluid as seen by a stationary (i.e., inertial) observer will be

$$\varepsilon = \pi\rho \int_0^R v^2(r) r \, dr$$

and the angular momentum

$$L = 2\pi\rho \int_0^R v(r) r^2 \, dr$$

where ρ is the density of the fluid and R the radius of the container.

Now if we minimize ε with respect to $v(r)$, we clearly obtain the frustrating result that $v(r)$ must be zero. This suggests that we consider the energy ε' of the fluid as seen by an observer who is rotating with the container at a steady angular velocity Ω.

Consider a pair of axes (x,y,z) and (x',y',z') in which the z and z' axes are coincident with the axis of the container. Let the $x'y'$ pair be in steady rotation about the z' axis at the velocity of the container Ω. Consider a point P in the xy plane whose radius vector in this plane is $\mathbf{r}$. We shall suppose point P is moving with velocity $\mathbf{v}(r)$ as seen by the stationary observer.

Now

$$\mathbf{r} = \mathbf{i}x + \mathbf{j}y = \mathbf{i}'x' + \mathbf{j}'y'$$

and
$$\mathbf{v}(r) = \dot{\mathbf{r}} = \mathbf{i}\dot{x} + \mathbf{j}\dot{y} = \mathbf{i}'\dot{x}' + \mathbf{j}'\dot{y}' + x'\dot{\mathbf{i}}' + y'\dot{\mathbf{j}}'$$

that is,
$$\mathbf{v}(r) = \mathbf{v}'(r) + \mathbf{j}'x'\Omega - \mathbf{i}'y'\Omega$$
$$= \mathbf{v}'(r) + \mathbf{\Omega} \times \mathbf{r}$$

Thus

$$\varepsilon = \pi\rho \int_0^R [v'(r) + \Omega r]^2 r\, dr$$

$$= \pi\rho \int_0^R v'^2(r) r\, dr + 2\pi\rho\Omega \int_0^R v'r^2\, dr + \pi\rho\Omega^2 \int_0^R r^3\, dr$$

$$= \pi\rho \int_0^R v'^2 r\, dr + 2\pi\rho\Omega \int_0^R (v - \Omega r) r^2\, dr + \frac{\pi\rho\Omega^2 R^4}{4}$$

$$= \pi\rho \int_0^R v'^2 r\, dr + \Omega L - \frac{2\pi\rho\Omega^2 R^4}{4} + \frac{\pi\rho\Omega^2 R^4}{4}$$

that is,
$$\varepsilon = \left(\pi\rho \int_0^R v'^2 r\, dr - \frac{\pi\rho\Omega^2 R^4}{4} \right) + \Omega L$$

But the expression enclosed in the parenthesis is ε'. To render this somewhat more transparent, consider first the term $(\pi\rho\Omega^2 R^4)/4$. This is the kinetic energy which the fluid would have if it were rotating as a solid body. But if the fluid were actually at rest, as seen by the inertial observer, this is precisely what the rotating observer would see because of his relative motion to the fluid. We must therefore subtract this term if we are to compare the energies as seen by the two observers. Hence, finally,

$$\varepsilon = \varepsilon' + \Omega L\dagger$$

---

† This result may be obtained in a more elegant and general way as follows. Consider a system of interacting particles whose potential energy is W. The Lagrangian function $\mathcal{L}$ will be

$$\mathcal{L} = \Sigma\tfrac{1}{2}mv^2 - W = \Sigma\tfrac{1}{2}mv'^2 + \Sigma mv'\Omega r + \Sigma\tfrac{1}{2}mr^2\Omega^2 - W$$

Thus
$$\varepsilon' = \pi\rho \int_0^R (v^2 r - 2\Omega v r^2)\, dv$$

and
$$\frac{\partial \varepsilon'}{\partial v} = \pi\rho \int_0^R (2vr - 2\Omega r^2)\, dr = 0$$

that is,
$$v = \Omega r$$

In words, then, the energy will be minimal provided the fluid is rotating as a solid body with the angular velocity of the containing vessel. Under these circumstances we shall have a spatially uniform line density of

$$A = \frac{2\Omega}{h/m} \cong 2{,}000\Omega \qquad \text{lines/cm}^2$$

It will be clear that the above analysis has implied a rather dense array of lines—it would obviously be untrue if we had only one or two vortex lines in the fluid. As we see, this requirement is met even at quite low speeds of rotation. Thus at $\Omega = 1$ rpm we have of the order of 200 lines/cm².

Now according to Feynman's guess the radius of the core of a vortex line is very tiny—perhaps 4 or 5 A. Thus in most of the volume of the fluid the microscopic velocity field, which is h/mr, is irrotational, i.e., $\nabla \times v_s = 0$. Thus two, at first sight, diametrically opposed ideas, namely, solid-body rotation and curl-free circulation, are made compatible. We note also that, in the near vicinity of the lines, the velocity field, which is superimposed on the steady rotation, is quite high—for instance, of the order of 15 m/sec at a distance of 10 A. The velocity field is illustrated in Fig. 53a.

Of course the above analysis is purely classical, which, since we are dealing with a supposed quantum effect, would appear to render it suspect. Actually ε and L should be replaced by the Hamiltonian and angular momentum operators in the Schrödinger equation. Such a

---

The momenta will be

$$p = \frac{\partial \mathcal{L}}{\partial v} = mv$$

$$p' = \frac{\partial \mathcal{L}}{\partial v'} = mv' + m\Omega r = m(v' + \Omega r) = mv = p$$

The Hamiltonian functions are

$$H = \Sigma pv - \mathcal{L} = \Sigma mv^2 - \mathcal{L}$$
$$H' = \Sigma p'v' - \mathcal{L} = \Sigma mv(v - \Omega r) + H - \Sigma mv^2$$
$$= H - \Omega L$$

calculation would, of course, be much more difficult and appears hardly worthwhile. Since most measurements which we undertake (of the angular momentum, for example) would be "coarse grained," we should hardly expect a very different result from that obtained above. It would be only when we observed a single, or a few, vortices that it would become likely that their possible quantum-mechanical structure would have to be taken into account.

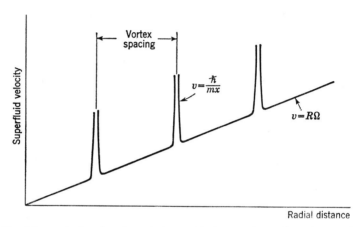

FIG. 53a. Schematic showing the velocity profile for rotating helium, illustrating the vortex-line fine structure.

It should be pointed out, however, that a somewhat better calculation (also classical) than the one above reveals that a strictly uniform line density does not occur for an equilibrium (i.e., minimum free energy) situation. It turns out that the line density is a little less than that given by our last formula. This is due to the fact that, near the boundary of the containing vessel, there is a perturbation in the density owing to the presence of "image vortices" in the boundary. However, this perturbation is negligibly small when we have a large number of vortices in the fluid.

These images, however, probably play an important role in one respect. Since they exert attractive forces on those vortices in the fluid adjacent to the boundary, they tend to inhibit the feeding of vortices into the fluid when the container is started into rotation. It is therefore quite possible that at low enough speeds and in the absence of any turbulence in the superfluid, no vortices will be fed into the fluid and consequently it will refuse to rotate.

SEARCH FOR THE QUANTUM OF CIRCULATION

Vinen[1] has devised an ingenious experiment aimed at demonstrating the existence of a quantum of circulation.   His apparatus consists of a fine wire (1 mil diam), clamped at each end, along the axis of a hollow tube approximately 5 mm in diameter.   The tube is filled with liquid helium, and both wire and tube may be rotated around the latter's axis.   A magnet, external to the cryostat, provides a uniform magnetic field perpendicular to the wire.   By sending a pulse of current down the wire, it may be set into transverse vibration at the natural frequency of its fundamental mode, i.e.,

$$\omega_0 = \frac{\pi}{l} \sqrt{\frac{T}{m}}$$

where ω_0 = angular frequency

T = tension in wire, which could be varied from outside cryostat

m = mass (per unit length) of wire

The idea behind the experiment is as follows.   In the absence of circulation in the liquid and around the wire, the frequency will be ω_0.   In the presence of circulation, however, the wire will experience an additional Magnus-effect force at right angles to the free motion of the wire.   This might be expected to alter the fundamental frequency ω_0.   This could be detected by observing the potential induced across the moving wire by the magnetic field.

In order to estimate whether such a frequency change would be measurable for a circulation as small as h/m_{He} we must analyze the situation as follows.   As is well known, the equation of motion (see Fig. 54 for notation) for the wire, in the absence of circulation, is

$$T \frac{\partial^2 x}{\partial z^2} = m \frac{\partial^2 x}{\partial t^2}$$

We note, however, that there are two possible directions of motion, i.e., the x and y directions, so that we have a second equation, identical to the above, for the y direction.   These familiar equations for a vibrating string have the well-known solutions, for the fundamental mode,

$$x = y = A \sin \omega_0 t \sin \frac{\pi z}{l} \tag{11}$$

In modern parlance, therefore, the system is doubly degenerate.

[1] W. F. Vinen, *Nature,* **181**:1524 (1958).

If now we admit a circulation K around the wire, the axis of the circulation and wire being coincident, the wire will experience a

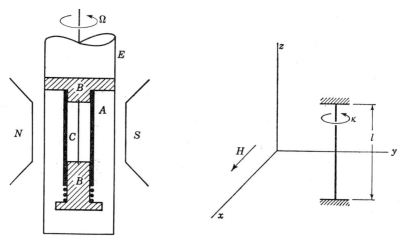

FIG. 54. The vibrating wire in the presence of a circulation K. E, can containing helium, which may be rotated at velocity Ω; A, insulated tube; C, fine wire; BB, blocks to hold wire under tension; NS, magnet poles. (*Vinen*, 1958.)

Magnus force,

$$\mathbf{f} = \rho(\mathbf{u} \times \mathbf{K}) \tag{12}$$

where u is the velocity of the wire. If we expand this product, we have

$$f_x = +\rho K \frac{\partial y}{\partial t}$$
$$f_y = -\rho K \frac{\partial x}{\partial t} \tag{13}$$

Thus the equation of motion of the wire now becomes

$$T \frac{\partial^2 x}{\partial z^2} + \rho K \frac{\partial y}{\partial t} = m \frac{\partial^2 x}{\partial t^2}$$
$$T \frac{\partial^2 y}{\partial z^2} - \rho K \frac{\partial x}{\partial t} = m \frac{\partial^2 y}{\partial t^2} \tag{14}$$

A possible solution for Eqs. (14) is[1]

$$x = A \sin \omega_1 t \sin \omega_2 \sin \frac{\pi z}{l}$$
$$y = A \cos \omega_1 t \sin \omega_2 t \sin \frac{\pi z}{l} \tag{15}$$

[1] A somewhat similar analysis is employed in the usual treatment of the Foucault pendulum.

Upon substituting these back into Eqs. (14), we find this is indeed a solution, provided

$$\omega_1 = \frac{\rho K}{2m}$$

$$\omega_2 = \sqrt{\frac{\pi^2 T}{l^2 m} + \omega_1^2}$$

When the vibrating wire moves across the lines of force of the steady magnetic field H, an alternating potential is developed along its length of amount

$$V = \int_0^l H_x \frac{\partial y}{\partial t}\, dz$$

Hence, using (15), we obtain

$$V = \frac{2HAl}{\pi} (\omega_2 \cos \omega_1 t \cos \omega_2 t - \omega_1 \sin \omega_1 t \sin \omega_2 t) \qquad (16)$$

Now because of the small size of the circulation for which we are searching, it follows that ω_1 can be made much smaller than ω_2. Thus we may neglect ω_1 in comparison to ω_2 in expression (16) and, under these circumstances,

$$\omega_2 \approx \omega_0 = \frac{\pi}{l} \sqrt{\frac{T}{m}}$$

Hence
$$V \cong 2HA \sqrt{\frac{T}{m}} \cos \omega_1 t \cos \omega_0 t \qquad (17)$$

The wire, in the absence of circulation in the helium, is tuned to its fundamental frequency $\omega_0/2\pi$ by sending a pulse of current through it by means of a condenser discharge. These free oscillations decay with time because of energy dissipation in the surrounding helium. After suitable amplification the oscillations are displayed on a C.R.O. For the experiment in question $\omega_0/2\pi$ was typically about 500 vib/sec.

For a single quantum of circulation, $\omega_1/2\pi$ amounted to about ¼ vib/sec. Thus, for such a quantum, the 500 pattern on the oscilloscope would be modulated by this lower frequency, very much like the familiar beats in acoustics. Further, this beat frequency is of sufficient magnitude to be accurately measurable. It thus appears that Vinen's experiment should be quite capable of detecting a single quantum of circulation, if such exists, by a most ingenious approach.

The procedure used in the experiment is typically as follows:
1. Rotate above the λ point until the helium is in equilibrium.
2. Cool very slowly to $\sim$1.3°K.
3. Measure the circulation with a small amplitude of vibration.

It is now necessary to inquire as to what speed of rotation is required to produce a single quantum of circulation. In line with our previous discussion, this requires that ε' be least. Suppose the liquid to possess a circulation around the wire of amount $N(h/m)$, where N is an integer. Then if the radius of the wire is a and that of the container b, we will have

$$\varepsilon' = \pi\rho \int_a^b rv^2\, dr - \pi\rho\Omega \int_a^b 2r^2v\, dr$$

Also

$$2\pi rv = N\frac{h}{m}$$

or

$$v = N\frac{h}{mr}$$

whence, on substitution, we obtain

$$\varepsilon' = \pi\rho N^2 \left(\frac{h}{m}\right)^2 \ln\frac{b}{a} - \pi\rho\Omega N \frac{h}{m}(b^2 - a^2)$$

We now wish to vary the speed Ω (and hence also N) such that ε' will be minimal, i.e.,

$$\frac{\partial\varepsilon'}{\partial N} = \pi\rho 2N \left(\frac{h}{m}\right)^2 \ln\frac{b}{a} - \pi\rho\frac{h}{m}(b^2 - a^2)\left(\Omega + N\frac{\partial\Omega}{\partial N}\right) = 0$$

that is,

$$\frac{d\Omega}{dN} = 2\Omega_0 - \frac{\Omega}{N}$$

wherein

$$\Omega_0 = \frac{h/m \ln(b/a)}{b^2 - a^2}$$

The above equation has as its solution

$$\Omega = N\Omega_0$$

Thus to produce a single vortex quantum ($N = 1$) we require, at least, a speed of rotation of Ω_0. Substituting the values of b ($\frac{1}{4}$ cm) and a ($\frac{1}{800}$ cm) into the expression for Ω_0, this yields a value just in excess of 7.5 rev/hr. Any lesser speed than this will produce no circulation; i.e., the superfluid will remain at rest.

The results of the experiment were not so "clean" as had been hoped. It was observed that circulations of the order of h/m_{He}, for angular velocities somewhat greater than Ω_0, did in fact occur; and, further, these circulations often persisted unchanged for periods as long as one or two hours after the rotation had stopped. On the other hand, the observed circulations were not always equal to integral multiples of h/m_{He}, often lying between one and two times this quantity. Further, it was found that when the helium was cooled below the

λ point *without rotation* a finite value of circulation (less than h/m_{He}) was observed.

It may be, of course, that our analysis is too naïve from the hydrodynamical viewpoint and the circulation pattern is more complicated than that envisaged above. Vinen presents some evidence in support of this and thinks it possible that a quantum of circulation could surround a certain length of the wire and then become detached as a free vortex line.

In any event, the fact that the observed circulation persists undiminished for times of the order of an hour is quite intriguing, as is the fact that it can *sometimes* be just h/m_{He}. All this suggests an unusual "thought" experiment. Suppose Vinen's apparatus were hung from a "frictionless" magnetic bearing of the type developed by Beams. Suppose further it were coasting, above the λ point, at a speed somewhat less than that required to produce one unit of circulation in the superfluid (Ω_0) and then cooled below the λ point. Clearly, above the λ point the fluid, being classical, will rotate as a solid body with appropriate angular momentum. Sufficiently far below the λ point ($\sim 1°K$) it will practically all be at rest, since the speed is insufficient to produce one quantum. The "lost" angular momentum will therefore show up as a torque on the apparatus, which will cause it to speed up. The low magnitude of Ω_0 probably precludes an actual successful trial.

SUPERFLUID WIND TUNNEL

An experiment aimed in the same general direction as the last one but of a very different nature has been reported by Craig and Pellam.[1] It has been known for many years that the lift produced on an airfoil by its motion through the fluid is a consequence of the Magnus effect. In a classical fluid vortices form and break away from the airfoil at its trailing edge; conservation of momentum requires a counter circulation round the system necessary for the Magnus effect. The above authors reasoned that, if the circulation is quantized in helium, so must the lift be.

Two technical problems presented themselves: first, to produce and measure a known velocity field in the superfluid; and second, to choose a system sufficiently sensitive that the small "lift quanta" could be resolved. Figure 55 shows a simplified diagram of their arrangement. The superfluid stream was produced by fountain effect, the normal fluid velocity being suppressed by superleak filters. The fluid velocity

[1] P. P. Craig and J. R. Pellam, *Phys. Rev.*, **108**:1109 (1957).

was measured by Bernoulli effect, using a miniature Venturi meter. The airfoil consisted of a small propeller, made of mica flakes, hung from a quartz torsion fiber. Thus lift was translated into a torque on the fiber which could be measured with the usual mirror, lamp, and scale arrangement.

The result (Fig. 56) showed no lift at all[1] up to a fluid velocity of about 0.6 cm/sec, after which point a finite lift, increasing with increasing fluid velocity, was observed. No evidence of quantization was found, which presumably ought to show up as a series of steps in the torque-velocity plot. Thus, up to a certain critical velocity, the flow for this geometry appears purely potential with no circulation and, as such, argues neither for nor against the idea of quantized circulation.

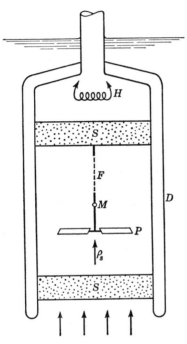

FIG. 55. Superfluid wind tunnel. H, electric heater; D, unsilvered Dewar; SS, superleaks; P, propeller; F, quartz fiber; M, mirror. (Craig and Pellam, 1957.)

ANGULAR MOMENTUM EXPERIMENTS

Walmsley and Lane[2] have attempted to measure the angular momentum of He II contained in a cylindrical vessel which is in steady rotation about its vertical axis of symmetry. In the case of a classical liquid the equilibrium rotational state would, as we have seen, be of the solid-body type with a corresponding angular momentum which we may term classical. For He II the Landau criterion of zero curl would, at first sight, prohibit this, but, as we have also seen, the Onsager-Feynman vortex theory overcomes this difficulty and again, for an equilibrium situation, predicts a classical result. Figure 57 presents a schematic diagram of the experimental arrangement. The cylindrical vessel I was hung from a torsion fiber B with the usual mirror F to observe deflections; B was

[1] Actually, in part of this velocity range, there was a slight negative lift which was attributed to the backflow of the normal component, which was not entirely suppressed by the superleak filters.

[2] R. H. Walmsley and C. T. Lane, *Phys. Rev.*, **112**:1041 (1958).

attached to the shaft of a small electric motor A.   The system included
a copper cylinder D situated between the poles of an electromagnet E.
The vessel I (the "bucket") could be filled with liquid helium from the
bath and the whole system then raised so that I was situated in the
vapor above the bath.

The bucket and contained He II were now rotated at constant speed
for a given (long) period of time via the motor (acting through the

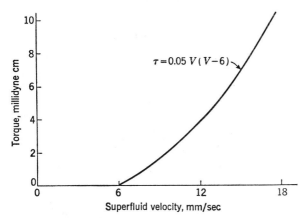

FIG. 56. Torque exerted on the propeller as a function of the velocity of the superfluid.   (*Craig and Pellam*, 1957.)

fine fiber B) at some fixed temperature below the λ point.   The purpose
of this was to bring the liquid in the bucket into rotational equilibrium,
of whatever state, with the latter.   Next the motor was stopped;
simultaneously, the suspension and bucket were also stopped by
switching a current on and then off in the magnet, thus using an eddy-
current brake.   This stopping operation was made as rapid as possible—
the order of ½ sec typically.   From this time forward the rotating
helium yielded up its angular momentum to the initially at rest bucket,
thereby producing a torque on the latter which could be measured
from the resulting deflection of the system.

Accordingly, the equation of motion of the suspended system is

$$\frac{d}{dt}\left(L + I_0\frac{d\varphi}{dt}\right) = -k\varphi - D\frac{d\varphi}{dt}$$

where L = angular momentum of liquid
   I_0 = moment of inertia of bucket system
   k = torsion-fiber constant
   D = frictional damping constant due to surrounding vapor
   φ = system deflection

Direct integration of this expression then gives

$$\Delta L = L(0) - L(T) = k \int_0^T \varphi(t)\, dt + I_0 \left(\left|\frac{d\varphi}{dt}\right|_T - \left|\frac{d\varphi}{dt}\right|_0 \right) \\ + D[\varphi(T) - \varphi(0)]$$

where T is time (long) measured from the end of the stopping operation. In the actual experiment the last two
terms on the right of the above equation were
always quite negligible compared to the first
one. Clearly, therefore, the *difference* in the
angular momenta of the He II at $t = 0$ and
$t = T$ could be found by observing the system
deflection φ as a function of time and perform-
ing the necessary integration.

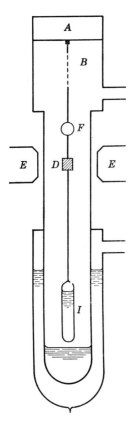

In actual practice the deflection of the light
spot was recorded on photographic paper, moving at constant speed, so that a plot of φ versus t was obtained. The integration was then
performed by area measurement. At this stage
we must resort to some assumptions which, while
plausible, are not certain; the most important of
these are as follows:

1. The system is rotated for a long enough
time, prior to stopping, so that all the He II
capable of being excited into rotation is in fact
doing so. This was made plausible by varying
the preparation time so that a value of ΔL was
reached such that longer times of preparation
did not change it. The time was the order of
35 min.

2. The duration of the run, after stopping,
was sufficiently long so that *all* the angular momentum of the liquid was yielded to the bucket.
This is not readily checkable, as will emerge.
The time was the order of 30 min.

3. The angular momentum yielded during
the braking period ($\frac{1}{2}$ sec) was assumed to be
negligible. This, also, is not readily checkable
but is fairly plausible, as will emerge.

FIG. 57. Schematic of
the arrangement used
to measure the angular
momentum of liquid
helium. (*Walmsley and
Lane*, 1958.)

If all the above assumptions are correct, or very nearly so, then the
measured quantity ΔL is indeed the angular momentum of He II at the
temperature and preparation speed of the experiment.

As a general over-all check, an identical series of runs were made with the helium above the λ point. Here not only must the angular momentum be truly classical, but it is also readily computed from the geometry, speed, and density of He I. Thus this computed result must agree with the measured ΔL unless the method is fallacious. The result did, in fact, show such agreement to within an experimental error

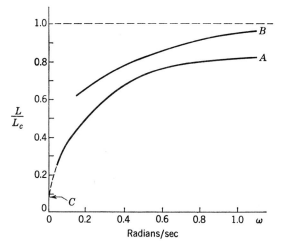

FIG. 58. The angular momentum ratio versus angular velocity at 1.4°K. Curve A is for a bucket radius of 11 mm, and curve B is for one of 8 mm; point C is the ratio of ρ_n/ρ at 1.4°K. (*Walmsley and Lane*, 1958.)

of around ± 10 per cent. This, however, while necessary is not sufficient. The hydrodynamics of He I and He II may differ substantially despite the fact that the kinematic viscosities are similar.

Figure 58 shows the ratio of ΔL (here tagged simply as L) to the classical value of the same (L_c) as a function of angular velocity for two different-sized buckets. The quantity L_c, of course, is computed from the known dimensions of the buckets, assuming solid-body rotation and the total density ρ for He II.

It will be appreciated that the measurement is a difficult one from the standpoint of sensitivity. At the lowest speeds the kinetic energy of rotation residing in the liquid is only $\sim 10^{-3}$ erg. Thus there is a good deal of scatter among the experimental points which the smoothed data of Fig. 58 do not show. This might explain why two buckets with only a small difference in radius (11 and 8 mm respectively)[1] show different results; this is possible but not certain.

[1] The difference in the radii of gyration of the two bucket "voids" is, however, substantial.

At any rate, the curves seem to "limit" properly; i.e., $L/L_c \to 1$ at high speeds (cf. Osborne's experiment) and $\frac{L}{L_c} \to \frac{\rho_n}{\rho}$ when $\omega \to 0$, which is also very reasonable. And, at face value, the result is diametrically opposed to the vortex-line picture.

The authors thought that this might be due to having measured a nonequilibrium situation. That is to say, for some reason, *less* than an equilibrium array of vortices are fed into the liquid by the preliminary rotation. To check this, a variation in procedure was tried. The bucket was first rotated at a "high" speed ($\sim$1 radian/sec) for a long time. It was then gradually decelerated to a "low" speed ($\sim$0.1 radian/sec) and, after the usual preparation time, the measurement was taken. The result was identical with that obtained by the usual procedure at 0.1 radian/sec.

To return to assumption 2, it is conceivable that, when the speed of rotation falls below a certain critical value, angular momentum is retained by means of a "persistent current" rather analogous to the persistent current of electrons flowing around a superconducting ring. If this were so, then some of the angular momentum would be "lost" in the sense that the above experiment would not detect it, and this loss would be the more serious at the lower speeds. In any event, the experiment, which appears to be of a fairly fundamental nature, would bear repeating with an improved and less crude technique, if possible.

As part of his hydrodynamical investigations, Lin,[1] taking the results for the larger bucket at face value, has proposed the following model. He proposes that, at a solid boundary (the bucket wall in this case), the following "boundary condition" holds:

$$\frac{\partial \mathbf{v}_s}{\partial N} = f(q^2)\mathbf{q}$$

wherein q is the tangential component of the difference between the superfluid velocity and the wall velocity and N is a direction normal to the wall. The function $f(q^2)$ must be determined from the experiments. If q is small, we may assume

$$f(q^2) = \alpha + \beta q^2 + \cdots$$

where α and β are constants. Now clearly, in the light of Andronikashvili's pile-of-discs experiment, α must be negligibly small. We note also, in the above formulation, that the Landau criterion (curl $\mathbf{v}_s = 0$) is abandoned.

[1] C. C. Lin, *Phys. Rev. Letters*, **2**:245 (1959).

The result shows

$$\frac{L}{L_c} = s + x(1 - s)$$

$$\frac{\omega}{\omega_H} = \frac{1}{2}\left[\frac{s}{(1 - s)^3}\right]^{1/2}$$

$$\omega_H{}^2 = \frac{4\beta}{a^3}$$

wherein $x = \rho_n/\rho$ and a is the bucket radius.   The above is in excellent agreement with the experimental values for the 11-mm bucket with $\omega_H = 0.17$ radian/sec.

Naturally, the truth of Lin's analysis[1] is crucially dependent on the correctness, or otherwise, of the experiment.   It will be noticed that the theory predicts a bucket-size effect which is, however, opposite to that found experimentally.   For reasons of sensitivity, however, the experimental data for the smaller bucket are much less satisfactory than those for the larger so that perhaps this point is still open.

MUTUAL FRICTION AND VORTEX WAVES

The concept of "mutual friction" between the normal and superfluid components in He II is an old one and was proposed originally by Gorter and Mellink to account for observed anomalies in the flow of helium through narrow slits.   The proposal is that an action-reaction pair occurs whenever the two fluids have a relative velocity with respect to each other.   If we feed into the hydrodynamic equations a term representing a force proportional to $(\mathbf{v}_n - \mathbf{v}_s)$ and solve for the second sound, we come out with a wave motion which is now attenuated in the direction of propagation.

This is, of course, precisely what Hall and Vinen found for their radial mode resonator when it was put in steady rotation.   This in turn suggests that a special type of mutual friction must be induced between the components by the rotational motion.   The question therefore arises as to what special mechanism can be imagined which might produce such a friction in the rotational state.   Hall and Vinen[2] take the rather bold step of applying the classical Magnus effect to the elementary vortex lines.

[1] The theory is also in good accord with some measurements by Atkins [*Proc. Phys. Soc.* (*London*), **A64**:833 (1951)] on the velocity of flow of He II through narrow tubes.

[2] H. E. Hall and W. F. Vinen, *op. cit.*, p. 215.

We recall that in their radial mode experiment the second sound is measured in the rotating system, and to such an observer, prior to switching on the second sound, the lines are at rest. The second sound produces an alternating counterflow (radially) of the superfluid and normal components. When the latter excitations (mainly rotons) collide with a line, they produce a force on it normal to its length. This Hall and Vinen show convincingly by computing the momentum changes when a roton interacts with a line, which shows also that the scattering is symmetrical in the forward direction. The resulting force (with an opposite reaction on the normal component), if unbalanced, would drive the vortices in the radial direction. The authors, however, assume that the force is balanced by a Magnus reaction, thereby giving the line a lateral velocity with respect to the bulk superfluid in which it exists. This, in turn, via the Bernoulli effect, produces a reaction force on the bulk superfluid equal and opposite to that produced on the normal fluid by the roton collisions.

While it is true that the above analysis is a none-too-happy blending of classical and quantum ideas, yet, as the authors point out, without some such mechanism it is exceedingly difficult to visualize how the force could be transmitted to the superfluid bulk at all.

A detailed calculation based on the above shows that the mutual friction force $\mathbf{F}_{sn}$ in the radial direction is given by

$$\mathbf{F}_{sn} \propto \frac{\omega}{\omega} \times [\omega \times (\mathbf{v}_s - \mathbf{v}_n)]$$

and the resulting computed attenuation coefficient for the second sound is in good agreement with the experimentally observed values for the radial mode resonator. Hence this is fairly firm evidence for the existence of vortex lines in He II, although it leaves the question of their quantization still open.

Motivated by the above ideas, Hall[1] has reported an Andronikashvili pile-of-discs type of experiment with superimposed steady rotation of the liquid. In this he had several parameters which could be varied, e.g., the period of the disc system, $2\pi/\Omega$, the disc spacing, and the angular velocity ω of the rotation. An increase in the period of the disc system, as compared with no rotation, was to be expected as a result of the dragging of the superfluid due to the mutual friction. The results, however, were quite surprising and vastly at variance with the above expectation.

It is convenient to express the measurements in terms of the ratio ρ'/ρ_s, where ρ' is the effective density of superfluid which moves with

[1] H. E. Hall, *Proc. Roy. Soc. (London)*, **A245**:546 (1958).

the discs. Thus with no rotation, ρ' should be zero, as Andronikashvili found. Among other things, Hall found, under certain conditions, a large *decrease* in the period of the disc system as a result of the superimposed steady rotation. This could only come about if at least some of the entrained superfluid were moving in a direction opposite to the motion of the discs![1] Hall observed that this curious behavior occurred only under two conditions, namely, (1) $\omega \ll \Omega$; (2) the disc surfaces, which were of mica, were artificially roughened. As a double check, an experiment under identical conditions but above the λ point showed no such behavior. In this case, in which ρ' was simply equal to ρ, the superimposed rotation had no effect whatever.

Hall's explanation of this curious effect is based on the hypothesis that vortex lines in the superfluid, created by the rotation, terminate on and are rigidly anchored to protuberances on the disc surfaces created by the roughening process. The motion of these lines through the bulk superfluid results in a Magnus force which, in turn, produces wave motions in them. This very neatly accounts for the negative ρ' since, with such standing waves, the motion of the lines (which are part of the superfluid) can clearly be in opposite phase with respect to the motion of the discs.

Hall subjects the above model to a detailed mathematical analysis in which the Magnus force is equated to that caused by the bending of the lines which are under tension.[2] Inertia effects of the line are ignored, since its effective mass is probably very small.

The result shows that the normal modes of vibration of the line which, as stated, is fixed to the discs at each end, are circularly polarized transverse vibrations whose wave numbers are given by

$$k_{\pm}^2 = -\left(\frac{2\omega \pm \Omega}{\varepsilon}\right)\rho_s \frac{h}{m}$$

wherein k_+ corresponds to a vibration in the same sense as the rotation and k_- in the opposite sense. As is the analogous case for a vibrating string, the calculation predicts resonance effects when the disc separation is an odd number of half-wavelengths, and this is found true

[1] That is to say, ρ' was negative.

[2] This tension is equivalent to the energy of a line per unit length, ε, i.e.,

$$\varepsilon = \int_a^b \frac{1}{2} 2\pi r \, dr \rho_s \left(\frac{\hbar}{mr}\right)^2$$
$$= \frac{\rho_s}{4\pi}\left(\frac{h}{m}\right)^2 \ln \frac{b}{a}$$

in which a is the radius of the hole in the center of the line and b is a distance of the order of the line spacing.

experimentally. Finally, by assigning a value to $\varepsilon m/\rho_s h$ of approximately 8.5×10^{-4} cm²/sec, an excellent fit to the experimental curves is obtained. Thus the experiment yields a value for the elementary vortex energy without, however, deciding one way or another on the question of quantization.[1] Apart from this, however, the experiment is so unusual that it would be hard to visualize any explanation different from that advanced by Hall. In this light it is perhaps the most convincing evidence, to date, for the existence of vortex lines in rotating He II.

SUMMARY OF THE PROBLEM OF ROTATION

We have discussed the principal work, up to the present, concerned with He II in uniform relation. Such properties as the second sound velocity appear to be quite unaffected even at comparatively high speeds,[2] and all of this is not in disagreement with the vortex-line picture. This model also accounts very nicely for the second sound work and appears nearly indispensable for an understanding of Hall's rotational Andronikashvili experiment.

On the other hand, the single experiment so far (Vinen's) which is, in principle, capable of detecting single quanta of circulation turned out to be inconclusive. At the same time the test for an equilibrium concentration of lines which ought to imitate solid-body rotation (Walmsley and Lane) failed to confirm this expectation.

These last two experiments are fairly fundamental to the Onsager-Feynman theories, and their "negative" results are, therefore, somewhat disappointing. We cannot help but suspect that, in both these cases, what we might call the hydrodynamics of the liquid plays an important role. In other words, the picture of a neat array of vortex lines in uniformly rotating helium is probably much oversimplified.

Above all, at the moment, we do not have any clear picture as to how, in rotating He II, a vortex line is created. In the Walmsley-Lane experiment, for example, the lines had to be created at 1.4°K, where 93 per cent of the liquid was in the superfluid phase. What role, if

---

[1] The energy value is some 25 per cent less than Feynman's earlier "guesstimate."

[2] There are additional superfluid effects which have been shown experimentally to be independent of rotation. Thus Andronikashvili and Kaverkin, in the rotating beaker experiment already cited, showed that the fountain effect was unaffected by rotation. More recently Snyder and Donnelly [*Phys. of Fluids*, **2**:408 (1959)] have, in a very difficult experiment, shown that the film flow rate out of a cylindrical vessel is independent of rotation in the range 4 to 220 radians/sec to within an error of 4 per cent.

any, did the remaining **7** per cent of classical liquid play in this? We have no idea since, for technical reasons, no experiment has been carried out at a sufficiently low temperature (say 0.2°K) at which we are quite sure that the normal component is negligible. Again, what is the role which surface protuberances in the containing vessel play? Would an "ideally smooth" surface lead to an absence of vortex lines? We have no experimental information of any kind on these questions.

All in all, it would seem that the amount of experimental effort so far invested in the Onsager-Feynman proposal is on the slim side, and it is quite possible that considerable dividends for the experimentalists are still in escrow.

SOME RECENT DEVELOPMENTS

Research on rotating He II is currently attracting a considerable amount of interest, and it seems desirable, therefore, to mention some very recent developments. As all this work is still in progress, there is a risk of being somewhat unfair to the authors concerned, since further experimentation may, of course, radically change their present views. Nevertheless, much of the work is so interesting that its current status deserves some mention.

Angular Momentum of He II[1]. This is a continuation of the problem considered by Walmsley and Lane, which was discussed previously, but now a quite different and, generally speaking, more satisfactory experimental technique is employed. The helium II is contained in a cylindrical glass bucket similar to that used in the previous work. This bucket is hung from a Beams-type magnetic suspension, the whole (bucket and contained helium) being surrounded by a high vacuum. Electromagnetic provision is made so that a small torque may be applied to the system for a short time. The bucket system is almost frictionless, and if the empty bucket is given a rotational impulse it will "coast" with negligible diminution in velocity for several hours.

With the bucket now containing helium at some low temperature ($\sim$1°K) it is given a short ($\sim\frac{1}{2}$ sec) rotational impulse and then allowed to coast freely. Observations of the bucket angular velocity, ω, as a function of time are then recorded, the initial speeds involved being in the range from 0.5 to about 2 rpm. Observations are carried out to about 10,000 sec. If we make the reasonable assumption that no angular momentum is communicated by the bucket to the super-

[1] J. D. Reppy, Behavior of Rotating Liquid Helium, Yale, 1960.

fluid during the very short acceleration period and if we neglect the very slight friction in the bearing, then clearly

$$I_b \omega_i = I_b \omega_f + L$$

Here I_b is the moment of inertia of the bucket and suspension, ω_i and ω_f the initial and final angular velocities of the bucket, and L the angular momentum acquired by the superfluid during the time of the experiment. Since I_b, ω_i, and ω_f are all measurable, the required quantity L is determined. The experiment is therefore conceptually very simple and clean.

To date, several types of behavior have been observed. Provided the experiment is given sufficient duration (of the order of 8,000 sec) the measured angular momentum is solid-body type, i.e., classical, at all initial speeds down to less than 1 rpm. This, of course, is in sharp disagreement with the results of Walmsley and Lane. In view of the long times involved in the new experiment it is possible that these authors did not extend their observations sufficiently far in time. In certain runs, however, a metastable state was found in which zero angular momentum was communicated to the superfluid during the entire course of the experiment—some 3 hr. In other words, the superfluid, being initially at rest, remained at rest. In other cases, the superfluid remained at rest for some 5,000 sec, whence it suddenly interacted with the bucket and acquired its full (i.e., classical) value of angular momentum in the ensuing 5,000 sec. The above is very reminiscent of the common phenomenon of supercooling in a liquid and, in the present instance, suggests that some turbulence was suddenly and accidentally induced in the helium from some outside source—perhaps an external vibration of the apparatus. This view is reinforced by the following variation of the experimental regime. A length of No. 40 wire, randomly twisted, was placed in the bucket, the volume occupied by the wire being less than 1 per cent of the volume occupied by the liquid helium. During the acceleration period it would be expected that this wire would stir up the liquid, i.e., introduce macroscopic turbulence into it.

Invariably the presence of the wire induced interaction between superfluid and bucket wall such that a classical angular momentum was observed; further, the time taken for the liquid to assume this angular momentum was much shorter.

It appears, therefore, that, by and large, the new experiment very nicely confirms the Onsager-Feynman viewpoint. Nevertheless, as Lin[1] has pointed out, it is not necessary to invoke such a massive thing

[1] C. C. Lin, private communication.

(on a molecular scale) as a quantized vortex line to account for the results.

Extension of Osborne's Experiment.   R. H. Meservey[1] has extended Osborne's experiment which, it will be recalled, measures the shape of the free surface of rotating helium, to much lower rotational speeds (~1 rpm).   To do this, he has spun a container (radius 1.3 cm) which, however, held only a shallow depth of liquid helium—around 43 μ depth.   The shape of the surface was then measured by an optical technique based on reflections from the liquid and substrate.   The results show a classical behavior; i.e., the superfluid rotates as a solid body, giving the classical parabolic profile.

Osborne's Disc Experiment.   This experiment, recently reported by Osborne,[2] is a very neat one and conceptually quite simple.   A cylindrical vessel containing helium rotates about a vertical axis along with a torsion head.   The latter has attached an oscillating-disc–torsion-fiber arrangement, similar to that used in the early viscosity measurements and carrying the usual mirror.   The plane of the disc is parallel to the plane bottom of the vessel, and both these surfaces are roughened.   Both disc and vessel rotate, and a photocell arrangement permits observation of the disc deflection despite the rotation of the whole.

In practice a steady external torque is applied to the disc system by electromagnetic means, and the resulting disc deflection is measured (1) with the system at rest and (2) with it in steady rotation.   In this latter case an array of line vortices, parallel to the rotation axis, should be anchored rigidly to the disc underface and the bottom of the vessel, respectively.   The idea that these lines are rigidly anchored appears to be the one assumption in the method but, because of the rough surfaces, it is certainly a reasonable one.

Thus as the disc is rotated from its equilibrium position these lines are stretched, and since they possess energy per unit length, this should result in a tension in the lines, i.e., an extra restoring torque over and above that imposed by the fiber.   The net result therefore should be that, for a given external torque, the deflection observed in the rotating case is less than that seen in the experiment when the system is at rest with, presumably, no vortices present.

The results do not fulfill this expectation in that no significant difference in the deflection in the two cases is observed.   This even though

[1] R. H. Meservey, An Optical Study of the Dynamics of Liquid Helium, Yale, 1960.

[2] D. V. Osborne, Seventh International Conference on Low Temperature Physics, Toronto, 1960.

the design of the experiment is such that the restoring torque due to the lines is about equal to that due to the fiber; i.e., the deflection should be halved in the rotating case.

If the helium in the apparatus is heated from 1.3 to 1.7°K and then cooled again to 1.3°K with the apparatus rotating all the while, a different result is sometimes, though not invariably, observed. In this regime the rigidity now becomes very large—some six times larger, for instance, than would be expected from the computation of the line tension.[1] Perhaps the most striking feature of this excess rigidity is that it persists after the rotation of the vessel has been stopped—for as long as 12 min without apparent change. It can be destroyed either by heating or by setting the disc into violent motion by means of an external torque.

To summarize (taking the results at face value), it appears that no lines are formed at 1.3°K ($\rho_n/\rho \sim 5$ per cent) by the simple act of rotation. Lines are formed only when the liquid is heated to 1.6°K ($\rho_n/\rho \sim 18$ per cent) and cooled again, and then they are much more rigid (i.e., possess much more energy) than the simple theory would allow. This creates in our minds the suspicion that the normal component may have something to do with the creation of the lines. No rotational experiment to date, of course, has been performed in which the normal density is really comfortably small. To do so, it would be necessary to operate at perhaps 0.4°K or lower, and this presents formidable technical difficulties. As a matter of fact, most experiments are carried out at the lowest convenient temperature (~ 1°K), and there is something to be said for future work in the higher temperature range. Alternatively one might "dope" the helium with He^3, thereby being able to control the normal-component density at a fixed temperature.

Rayleigh-disc Experiment. Pellam[2] has recently reported a rotational experiment which makes use of the Rayleigh-disc technique. The usual rotational vessel (diam 5 cm) contains a 3-mm disc (with

---

[1] As we know, the velocity field of a single vortex line is $v = \hbar/mr$. Further, there are $\dfrac{2\Omega}{h/m}$ lines/cm² when the vessel is rotating at speed Ω. The energy of a line (per unit length) is accordingly

$$\varepsilon = \pi\rho_s \int_a^b v^2 r \, dr = \pi\rho_s \frac{\hbar^2}{m^2} \ln \frac{b}{a}$$

where a is the core radius and b is the average line spacing, i.e., $\dfrac{1}{b^2} \approx \dfrac{2\Omega}{h/m}$. The tension in the line is the derivative of its total energy with respect to its length, i.e., it is ε. The main uncertainty lies in the value of the core radius a.

[2] J. R. Pellam, *Phys. Rev. Letters*, **5**:189 (1960).

its plane vertical) attached to a torsion fiber. The disc system is stationary; that is to say, it does not rotate with the helium vessel. Provision is also made such that the disc system may be centered at will at various positions along the radius of the rotating beaker.

As we know, Pellam, in his earlier work, proved that the Rayleigh disc is sensitive to the normal-component velocity field as well as that of the superfluid component (see Chap. 4), the torque on the disc, with either fluid, being proportional to the square of the fluid velocity. Thus the disc would appear to constitute a sensitive method for detecting and measuring superfluid velocities on a semimicroscopic scale.

When the vessel is set in rotation, at a given temperature, it only slowly achieves an equilibrium value—typically some half an hour— and this time delay is the longer the closer the disc is placed to the rotational axis. This is reasonable since it takes time for the velocity field created at the wall of the beaker to move into the body of the liquid.

When, however, the equilibrium value of the torque on the disc, kept at a fixed distance from the rotational axis and with a constant speed of rotation, is plotted as a function of the temperature, a quite remarkable behavior is observed. Above the λ point the torque is constant, as it should be under these conditions, for a classical liquid. At the λ point the torque now drops to zero! As we proceed to lower temperatures, the torque rises again monotonically. In the He II region the torque versus temperature curve is of the same general form as the well-known ρ_s/ρ curve as determined by Andronikashvili and others.

In the light of all previous rotation experiments this result is truly remarkable. At face value it appears to say that in He II but not in He I the superfluid component is in motion while the normal component is not! Even stranger is the result that, immediately upon passing the λ point, the angular momentum present in the classical He I suddenly vanishes. As the author emphasizes, it is clearly too early in the research to form any definite opinions.

CHAPTER 7

He^3 Solutions

Helium possesses only one stable isotope (He^3, discovered in 1939), and this exists naturally in extremely minute amounts. The development of reactor technology, however, has created a fairly abundant source via the following process:

$$_3\text{Li}^6 + _0n^1 \rightarrow _1\text{H}^3 + _2\text{He}^4$$
$$_1\text{H}^3 \xrightarrow{\beta} _2\text{He}^3$$

In the first reaction the tritium-helium separation is comparatively simple since the atoms are chemically different. The radioactive tritium then decays to He^3 by β-negative emission with a half-life of about 12.5 yr. Thus all one requires is a copious source of neutrons plus some patience.

The U.S. Atomic Energy Commission currently makes pure He^3 available, in roughly 1 liter STP amounts, at a price of around \$1.50 per cubic centimeter. A liter of the gas will liquefy to about 1.5 cm^3, which is a small but usable amount for many experiments.

In accordance with our previous discussion of the theory of super-fluidity, we should not expect pure He^3 to be a superfluid due to the statistics (Fermi) which the nuclei obey. Experimentally this appears to be correct. Careful measurements on the specific heat of pure He^3 down to 0.1°K reveal nothing in the way of a specific-heat jump with which we associate a λ point. Pure He^3, therefore, is not germane to the subject matter of this book.

On the other hand, liquefied mixtures of He^3 and He^4 do exhibit superfluidity with a whole series of λ points which are the lower the greater the He³ concentration.

EARLY EXPERIMENTS ON DILUTE He³ MIXTURES

For a considerable period after 1945, government He³ was not available, and therefore the naturally occurring isotope had to be used in experimental work. The usual source was the so-called "atmospheric helium." Helium is present in minute amounts in the earth's atmosphere, and the large-scale industrial production of liquid oxygen and nitrogen yields some helium as a byproduct. The helium generally employed in cryogenics comes from natural-gas wells (well helium) and is very much more abundant. The atmospheric helium contains He³ to the extent of about 1 part per million—a dilute source indeed. Nevertheless, early experimenters carried out some interesting work with this material.

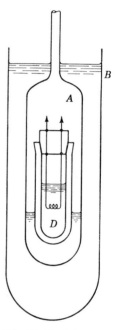

In 1947 Daunt et al.[1] carried out the following experiment (Fig. 59). In the Dewar B containing ordinary liquid helium below the λ point a vessel A contained the isotopic mixture. A second vessel D consisted of a small Dewar fitted with a ground-glass plug which formed a superleak, together with an electric heater. The experiment was made in two ways. First, the level in A was above the plug—any superfluid then drained through the superleak into D via gravity. Alternatively, the level in A was below the plug and heat was applied to the heater. D then filled via a superfluid film of liquid, approximately 10^{-6} cm thick, which passed readily through the plug. The latter, however, formed a sufficiently tight fit so that only a negligible amount of vapor could pass it.

FIG. 59. Test for participation of He³ in superflow. (*Daunt et al., 1947.*)

The liquid collected in D was evaporated (after that which remained in A had been removed), and the gas was sampled with a mass spectrometer. The result, in both cases, showed that the liquid in D contained less He³ than the original mixture. This was fairly good evidence that He³, at least in these concentrations, did not take place in superfluid flow.

[1] Daunt, Probst, Johnston, Aldrich, and Nier, *Phys. Rev.*, **72**:502 (1947).

As stated, the source available was extremely dilute, and the mass spectrometry was considerably pushed in analyzing even the source material, let alone the still more dilute liquid in D. Hence the experiment suffers from some lack of accuracy. In addition, more recent work[1] has shown that, generally speaking, superleaks are not entirely impermeable to He[3] atoms.

HEAT-FLUSH EFFECT

In 1948 Lane et al.[2] reported an experiment of a different nature; the idea behind this method was rather fundamentally based on the two-fluid hypothesis. In this case, as we have seen, any temperature gradient in bulk He II produces an internal convection such that the superfluid component flows toward the heat source and a balancing normal flow occurs in the reverse direction.

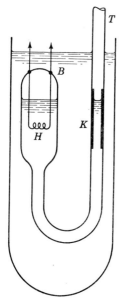

Thus in the presence of a thermal gradient, He[3] should be "trapped" by the normal component and flow with it but be ignored by the superfluid stream. The net effect, then, in an initially homogeneous mixture, should be to "flush" the He[3] in the direction of the heat current (i.e., with the normal stream) and so concentrate it in the colder regions of the apparatus. Thus we would have a richer source of He[3] to sample, as compared with the original gas, with a corresponding gain in accuracy.

A sketch of the apparatus originally used to test this idea is shown in Fig. 60. The glass capillary T had a metal section K and ended in a glass bulb B containing an electric heater H. The isotopic mixture had a free surface in B and K as shown. The heat path was therefore through the isotopic mixture from B to K, whence it exited to the surrounding helium bath held at some constant temperature. Hence by evaporating (by pumping) some gas from the free surface in K and analyzing with a mass spectrometer, a test of the validity of the ideas could be made.

FIG. 60. Heat-flush experiment. (*Lane et al.*, 1948.)

[1] K. R. Atkins and D. R. Lovejoy, *Can. J. Phys.*, **32**:702 (1954).
[2] Lane, Fairbank, Aldrich, and Nier, *Phys. Rev.*, **73**:256 (1948).

Samples from K were taken both with and without a heat current, and the result showed that, in the former case, the He³ concentration was more than one hundred times that in the unrefrigerated gas mixture, as against only two or three times richer in the absence of a heat current. Thus the method not only provided a possible tool for producing "rich" sources of He³ but also proved, in a particularly unambiguous manner, that He³ did not partake in the superfluid flow of He II.

At the time this was thought to constitute a clear-cut victory for the "statistics" approach to the theory of liquid helium, but a little later Landau and Pomeranchuk[1] showed, on theoretical grounds, that the method should work equally well on any dilute concentration of "foreign atoms" (e.g., electrons, He⁴ ions, He⁶ atoms, etc.) dissolved in the helium. This has very recently been shown to be true by Careri and coworkers,[2] who succeeded in heat flushing He⁴ ions and electrons.

Beenakker et al.[3] have investigated the heat-flush mechanism in somewhat greater detail. If even large heat currents are made to flow in He II, the resulting temperature gradient is, as we know, extremely small, thus reflecting the enormous effective thermal conductivity of the fluid due to internal convection. These authors found that even slight amounts of He³ ($\sim$1 per cent) greatly decrease the conductivity of the liquid. The mechanism appears to be as follows. The heat current produces a concentration gradient of He³ such that the latter tries to accumulate at the cold region. This, in turn, produces a back pressure, since the He³ tries to rediffuse. This in turn leads to a balancing fountain pressure and hence an extra temperature gradient. Thus the presence of the He³ gives rise to a larger temperature gradient than would occur in pure He II; i.e., the thermal conductivity is reduced.

On the basis of the above work, W. M. Fairbank has made the

[1] L. Landau and I. Pomeranchuk, *Compt. rend. acad. sci. U.S.S.R.*, **59**:669 (1948).

[2] Careri, Reuss, Scaramuzzi, and Thomson, Proceedings Madison Conference, 1958, p. 155. An interesting early observation by Savich and Shalnikov [*J. Phys. (U.S.S.R.)*, **10**:299 (1946)], which they were unable to explain, is probably due to the effect. Some hydrogen gas was allowed to enter the helium Dewar while above the λ point, and the hydrogen solidified and formed a "fog" of ice particles dispersed through the liquid. Upon cooling through the λ point, the particles were observed to coagulate at the surface. Since the latter would be somewhat cooler than the bulk liquid, because of the pumping, the heat flush carrying the ice would be in this direction.

[3] Beenakker, Taconis, Lynton, Dokoupil, and van Soest, *Physica*, **18**:433 (1952).

interesting suggestion that such a dilute mixture, contained in a fine tube of poorly conducting material, could be used as an automatic heat switch (see Chap. 1) in magnetic cooling experiments.

λ-TEMPERATURES

The fact that He^3 does not participate in the superfluid-component motion carries with it an important implication. The lambda temperature may be defined as that for which $\rho_n/\rho = 1$. We recall that, on this basis, Landau computed $T_\lambda = 2.13°K$ from his theory. But in view of the above, the net effect of added He^3 is to increase the normal-fluid concentration, and so the ratio ρ_n/ρ will approach unity sooner, i.e., at a lower temperature. Thus the solutions ought to have a whole series of λ points being the lower the higher the He^3 concentration.

In 1949, when reactor-produced He^3 first became available, Abraham, Weinstock, and Osborne[1] made some measurements on this point by observing the flow of the superfluid through a superleak. Above the λ point of a given mixture no (or very slight) flow occurs; below, however, the flow becomes very strong because of the passage of the superfluid component. Hence this method is a fairly sensitive one.

The results showed that the lambda temperature does depend on concentration, as expected; typically it is 2.04°K for a 2.4 per cent solution, dropping to 1.56°K for a 28.2 per cent mixture. We might suppose offhand that this process goes on indefinitely—the higher the He^3 concentration the lower the lambda transition. It turns out, however, that things are not quite so simple as that, as will emerge in due course. Below about 0.8°K all the solutions have two λ points corresponding to a spatial phase separation of the mixtures.

VAPOR-LIQUID EQUILIBRIUM

In a two-component system, e.g., alcohol-water or liquid air, the relative concentrations in the vapor and liquid phases are different. This is substantially a result of the fact that the vapor pressures of the two components differ. Since, as we know, the vapor pressures of pure He^3 and pure He^4 are quite different at a given temperature, we should expect the same effect in the isotopic mixtures—an assumption which is borne out by experiment.

One type of experiment, which has often been used by physical chemists, consists of condensing a gas mixture (whose composition is

[1] Abraham, Weinstock, and Osborne, *Phys. Rev.*, **76**:864 (1949).

known) in a glass bulb such that a free surface occurs. This is allowed to sit for some time, at a given temperature; then a small sample of the vapor is withdrawn and analyzed. The corresponding composition of the liquid in equilibrium with this vapor can then be computed from the necessary conservation of mass.

This kind of experiment, with He³-He⁴ solution, has been tried many times. Above the solution λ point the results were always consistent, showing that the He³ concentration in the vapor was greater

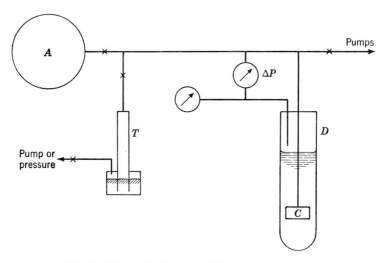

FIG. 61. Schematic diagram of Sommers's apparatus.

than that in the liquid. Below the λ point, however, the method often gave absurd results. For instance, for dilute solutions, it apparently showed that the He³ concentration in the vapor was zero! Since the method always works well classically, this effect constituted a considerable puzzle to the early workers in the field.

The reasons for the anomaly became clear only after the discovery of the heat-flush effect, because the unavoidable temperature gradients were such as to drive all the He³ away from the free surface which was in contact with the vapor to be sampled. In consequence, we shall ignore all this earlier work and discuss the work of Sommers,[1] which avoided all these pitfalls and is quite definitive.

Figure 61 shows, schematically, the arrangement adopted by him. Sommers measures the difference in pressure, ΔP, between the solution vapor and that of pure He⁴ under two distinct conditions:

[1] H. S. Sommers, *Phys. Rev.*, **88**:113 (1952).

1. Small measured masses of gas are continuously introduced into the experimental chamber and a plot is made of the mass versus ΔP (Fig. 62). The whole is carried out, of course, with a helium bath surrounding the chamber held at a fixed temperature. At the sharp break in the curve the mixture has just commenced to form liquid, since beyond this much more mass has to be added to produce a given change in the ΔP, because the liquid is much denser than the vapor.

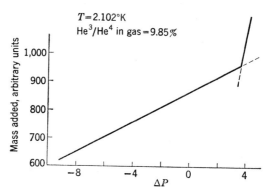

FIG. 62. Dewpoint experiment with He³-He⁴ mixtures. (*Sommers*, 1952.)

Now, at the break, the amount of liquid is extremely small, and, although it has a different composition from the surrounding vapor, the amount of He³ it has withdrawn is negligible. Hence the composition of the vapor (which is in equilibrium with this droplet) is the same as the known composition of the unrefrigerated gas.

2. Next, sufficient gas is fed to the chamber such that it is entirely filled with liquid up into the connecting capillary, and ΔP is again measured. Here the above argument works in reverse. The mass of equilibrium vapor is now so tiny that substantially all the He³ in the feed gas (which is known) is in the liquid. Thus if we call C_V the atomic ratio of He³ to He⁴ in the vapor and C_L the corresponding quantity for the liquid, we know these two quantities at various ΔP's and temperatures. We note also that the heat-flush disturbance is almost completely eliminated except perhaps for the very weakest solutions.

Now the ΔP, as defined above, must be the same for case 1 and case 2 for an equilibrium situation, i.e., liquid in equilibrium with its saturated vapor. A typical result is shown in Fig. 63 for the temperature $T = 1.300°K$, which represents a whole series of runs at this temperature, using a series of different gas mixtures. Here the true vapor pressure is plotted—this, of course, we readily obtain from the

ΔP's by adding the known vapor pressure of pure He⁴. It is clear that from such curves, evolved at different temperatures, we can obtain the ratio C_V/C_L as a function of temperature and at any fixed value of C_L simply by finding those points on the vapor lines which are at the same pressure as those points on the liquid lines which are cut by the ordinate drawn at the chosen value of C_L. A typical curve for the value $C_L = 5.5$ per cent is shown in Fig. 64.

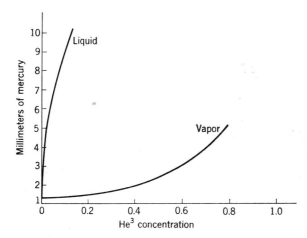

FIG. 63. Phase diagram for He³-He⁴ solutions at 1.3°K. (*Sommers*, 1952.) A solution having a vapor pressure of 5 mm at 1.3°K, for example, would have about 2 per cent He³ in the liquid and nearly 80 per cent He³ in the vapor.

It might, at first sight, be expected that since these solutions are mixtures of chemically identical isotopes, they should be "ideal." By an ideal solution is meant the following:

1. The vapor may be considered an ideal gas and as such obeys Dalton's law of partial pressures.

2. The liquid obeys Raoult's law.[1]

---

[1] This states that in a two-component mixture, containing in the liquid phase n_1 and n_2 atoms, respectively, the partial pressures in the vapor (p_1 and p_2, respectively) are given by

$$p_1 = \pi_1 x_1$$
$$p_2 = \pi_2 x_2$$

where $x_1 = n_1/(n_1 + n_2)$, $x_2 = n_2/(n_1 + n_2)$; i.e., $x_2 = 1 - x_1$ and π_1 and π_2 are the saturated vapor pressures of the *pure* components. Sometimes, in the literature, the first of these equations is called "Henry's law," while the second is given the name of Raoult.

On this basis it becomes an elementary calculation to show that

$$\frac{C_V}{C_L} = \frac{\pi_3}{\pi_4}$$

where the subscripts 3 and 4 refer to He³ and He⁴ respectively, and $C_V = (n_3/n_4)_{\text{vapor}}$ and $C_L = (n_3/n_4)_{\text{liquid}}$. Since both π_3 and π_4 have been accurately measured as a function of temperature, this result can be compared with Sommers's measurements, remembering, however, that it is expected to apply only to dilute mixtures. The agreement is poor, as is indicated in Fig. 64.

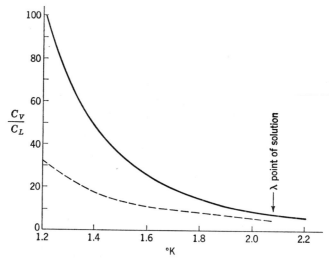

FIG. 64. C_V/C_L ratio versus temperature for He³-He⁴ at a constant value of $C_L = 5.5$ per cent. (*Sommers*, 1952.) The dotted line is that for an ideal solution.

Actually this is not very surprising, since the molar volumes of the two isotopes are very different and therefore do not simply exchange places with one another. Thus, replacing an He⁴ atom by an He³, the zero-point energy, for instance, will be increased by a factor of around ⁴⁄₃. As a result, the "cell" containing the He³ atom increases somewhat in size, and the energy of the neighboring He⁴ atoms is changed. We should therefore expect a change of volume on mixing and also a "heat of mixing." Of course no such effects occur for an ideal solution.

A considerable amount of effort has been put into evolving a theory to account for Sommers's results, and none of these is really satisfactory. Sommers, in his original paper, made use of purely classical solution theory (due to Van Laar). This is based on the next higher approximation to ideal solutions and makes use of the van der Waals equation, the constants in which are deduced via the observed critical constants for the two gases. This results in a not-too-bad agreement with the observations—certainly as good as found with any other theory.

The Van Laar theory, in addition to predicting a heat of mixing, also predicts a separation of the liquid solution into two phases below a certain critical temperature.[1]

HEAT OF MIXING

Sommers, Keller, and Dash[2] have made a direct determination of the heat of mixing W, for an 8.6 per cent solution of He³ in He⁴.

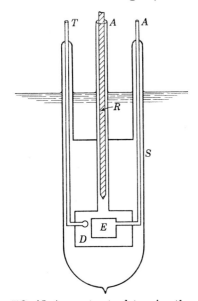

FIG. 65. Apparatus to determine the heat of mixing of He³ in He⁴. AA, filling tubes; T, He³ vapor-pressure-thermometer tube; D, He⁴ vessel; E, He³ vessel; R, tungsten wire; S, vacuum shield. (*Sommers et al.,* 1953.)

Figure 65 shows their arrangement. The pure He³ (0.1 cm³) and the pure He⁴ (1.0 cm³) occupied separate glass bulbs in what amounted to an adiabatic calorimeter. Both liquids were cooled to approximately 1°K, and the He³ bulb was broken by a tungsten wire operated from outside the cryostat. Temperatures were then observed on a separate He³ vapor-pressure thermometer, previously calibrated. Figure 66 shows the result of a typical run starting at $T = 1.02$°K. When the seal is broken, it is seen that the temperature of the mixture rapidly falls (indicating a *positive* heat of mixing) and then slowly warms up again because of the unavoidable heat leak into the apparatus, which is partly due to film reflux through the filling tubes. By extrapolating this heat leakage back to zero time, an initial low temperature, due to absorption of the heat of mixing from the solution, is found to be 0.78°K. The mixing heat for this solution is estimated by the authors as 0.17 cal/mole. We see, there-

[1] This temperature is given by

$$RT_c = \frac{W}{2}$$

where W is the heat of mixing.

[2] Sommers, Keller, and Dash, *Phys. Rev.,* **92**:1345 (1953).

fore, that the prediction of a positive heat of mixing is confirmed, although the experimental value is only about $\frac{2}{3}$ of that predicted by the Van Laar theory.

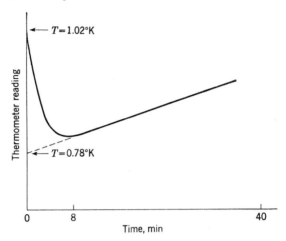

FIG. 66. Temperature curve obtained by adiabatically mixing He^3 and He^4 at an initial temperature of 1.02°K. (*Sommers et al.*, 1953.)

PHASE SEPARATION

As we have seen, the classical solution theory, which is at least order-of-magnitude correct, predicts a spatial phase separation of the two components, below some critical temperature, when there is a positive heat of mixing. This curious situation can perhaps be understood by the following simple model. In the vicinity of absolute zero we may not have such a mixing heat, else we should, in principle, be capable of reaching the absolute zero or even going beyond it. Thus the solution has to find some way out of this dilemma, and, other things being equal, it will choose the "cheapest," i.e., the least energetic. Now dilute solutions of either component as the solute, behave ideally, and ideal solutions have no heat of mixing. Thus the easiest thing for the solution to do is to separate into two dilute phases, i.e., one rich in He^3 and the other rich in He^4.

The phase separation was found experimentally by Walters and W. M. Fairbank[1] in 1956, and the critical temperature turned out to be a little above 0.8°K. To sample the solutions, they made use of the modern tool of nuclear magnetic resonance.[2] Since the He^3

[1] G. K. Walters and W. M. Fairbank, *Phys. Rev.*, **103**:262 (1956).

[2] For details of this technique see E. R. Andrew, "Nuclear Magnetic Resonance," Cambridge University Press, New York, 1955.

nucleus has a magnetic moment (spin $\frac{1}{2}$) while the He⁴ does not, this permitted them to identify the He³ in the mixture and also to determine their relative concentration from the amplitude of the induced voltage in a coil caused by the precessing nuclei in a steady magnetic field.

The He³-He⁴ solution was contained in a small vessel which was hung by a copper rod from a paramagnetic salt. The vessel was divided, vertically, into three compartments joined by small holes, and a slight vertical gradient was imposed on the steady magnetic field. Since the precession frequency depends linearly on the magnetic field strength, three "resonance lines" would, in consequence, be obtained in this geometry.

Below about 0.8°K the authors found that the amplitude of this signal from the lowest container was much less than that from the highest, indicating, therefore, that the upper one was much richer in He³ than the lower. By observing this effect during the warmup of a demagnetization, they were accordingly able to deduce a phase diagram for the spatial separation of the isotopes; the He³-rich phase, being the lighter, floated on top. This result is shown in Fig. 67.[1]

There is an interesting side light in connection with this work. Daunt and Heer in 1950[2] had measured the λ temperatures of a series of solutions by the following technique. A capillary tube (of poor heat-conduction material) with the ends closed was placed vertically in a magnetic cooling cryostat. Two salt pills, one above the other, were attached to it. A little He³-He⁴ mixture of known composition was condensed in the tube (the liquid interface being at the lower salt) and the two salt pills demagnetized to somewhat different temperatures, the upper (acting as a "heat block" down the tube) being at the higher temperature. The temperature of the lower pill was then observed as a function of time, i.e., a warmup curve evolved. It was found that, at some particular temperature, depending on the He³ concentration, there was a distinct "break" in this curve.

Daunt and Heer interpreted this break temperature as the λ point of the solution, using the following argument. When the solution is

---

[1] Acting, no doubt, on the principle of "seein's believin'," Peshkov and Zinovieva [*Soviet Phys. JETP*, **5**:1024 (1957)] repeated the experiment using an He³ refrigerator and directly viewing the mixture in a glass vessel. Because of the difference in refractive index between the two phases, the demarcation line between them is, under such conditions, clearly visible. These authors were unable to remix the phases by shaking the cryostat, thereby demonstrating a high degree of stability for the separation.

[2] J. G. Daunt and C. V. Heer, *Phys. Rev.*, **79**:46 (1950).

superfluid (i.e., below its λ point), a thin mobile film of superfluid coats the tube. Under the action of the upward temperature gradient this film, like all superfluid, moves up the tube until it reaches a point equal to its λ temperature. It then can no longer exist and so evaporates, the gas returning down the tube and recondensing at the liquid surface at the lower salt, there yielding its heat of condensation. But above the solution λ point this effect does not happen. Hence below its

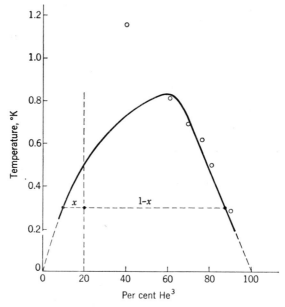

FIG. 67. He³-He⁴ phase separation. (*Walters and W. M. Fairbank*, 1956.) Circles are the λ-point determinations of Daunt and Heer (1950).

λ point we get what looks like an added heat leak over and above the normal conduction down the tube. At the solution λ point, therefore, we should get a break in the warming-up curve as observed. The results of this, for a number of concentrations, are also plotted in Fig. 67. In the Daunt-Heer experiment, it is the He³-rich phase which, being lighter, is at the liquid-vapor interface in the tube and so provides the film flow; a fact unknown, of course, to the authors at the time. The two results are seen to be in very good accord.

As in all equilibrium situations the two phases coexist at the same temperature. Thus, for example, a 20 per cent solution of He³ in He⁴ would, upon having its temperature lowered below about 0.5°K (see diagram), split into two phases. At 0.3°K, for instance, one phase would contain about 10 per cent He³ and the other about 88 per cent He³. By mass conservation it is easy to show that, of 1 g of the original mixture, a fraction x would become rich in He³ and the remainder $(1 - x)$ would be dilute; this is the well-known lever rule.

SECOND SOUND IN THE SOLUTIONS

As we have seen, the heat flush provides us with strong evidence that the He³ atoms move with the normal component in dilute solutions or, in other words, these atoms add to the normal fluid. Further, at temperatures below 1°K ρ_n/ρ in pure He⁴ becomes increasingly tiny, amounting to only approximately 1 per cent at 1°K.[1] Since ρ_n is intimately connected with the second-sound-wave propagation, two questions arise. First, how does the second sound behave at temperatures well below 1°K where ρ_n has practically vanished, and second, how do even minute amounts of He³, added to the He II, affect this behavior?

In order to arrive at satisfactory answers we might begin by inquiring as to what prediction the tried and true Landau theory has for the first situation. We recall that, at these low temperatures, the excitations are very largely phonons, the temperature dependence of the density of which goes at T^4 (see Chap. 5). Also the specific heat, of course, goes as T^3. Thus

$$c = \alpha T^3$$

$$S = \int \frac{c\, dT}{T} = \frac{\alpha}{3} T^3$$

$$\frac{\rho_n}{\rho} = \frac{4}{3v^2} E_{ph} = \frac{4}{3v^2} \int c\, dT = \frac{\alpha}{3v^2} T^4$$

where α is a constant and v is the velocity of first sound. Recalling also the second sound velocity,

$$u_2{}^2 = \frac{\rho_s}{\rho_n} \frac{TS^2}{c}$$

we get

$$u_2 = \frac{1}{3} \sqrt{3v^2 - \alpha T^4}$$

whence

$$\lim_{T \to 0} u_2 = \frac{v}{\sqrt{3}}$$

[1] It is of the order of 10⁻⁶ at 0.3°K.

From the extrapolated value of the measured velocity of first sound at 0°K this turns out to be about 137 m/sec, which is some seven times larger than the maximum velocity of u_2 above 1°K.

The experimental search for this effect has had a somewhat long and troublesome history. The first scientists to look for this in a satisfactory manner[1] showed that u_2 did indeed rise steadily below 1°K, and, on the basis of an extrapolation from about 0.1°K to the absolute zero, it looked as though u_2 might approach $v/\sqrt{3}$ as a limit.

Subsequent investigation, however, by de Klerk, Hudson, and Pellam[2] among others has shown this to be unlikely. The most probable situation is that as $T \to 0$, $u_2 \to v$. As a matter of fact, below about 0.4°K where the phonon mean free path begins to approach the dimensions of the apparatus we cease to get a true second sound wave at all and, instead, get a density wave in the "gas of phonons" which, of course, travels with an appropriate speed v. This occurs, of course, if we use a pulse technique which all the above workers employed. Osborne[3] has tried using continuous-wave resonance methods at these low temperatures, but, in line with the above, was unable to find resonances below about 0.5°K. In general we may therefore say that the second sound in pure He[4] ceases to exist below about 0.5°K where ρ_n/ρ is of the order of 10^{-5}.

While this has been a rather lengthy digression, it points up the fact that it would appear plausible that even very minute admixtures of He[3] might well produce quite startling changes in the second sound, which indeed turns out to be the case. Of course we must continually bear in mind that the He[3] atoms do not simply "replace" the phonons and rotons. For one thing, the number of atoms is fixed in a given concentration, whereas the number of phonons and rotons is not—they can be created and annihilated.

Lynton and H. A. Fairbank and, later, King and Fairbank[4] were the first to study the effects of He[3] on the second sound. Since the solutions were dilute and the investigators were anxious to avoid inhomogeneities due to heat flush, they employed the pulse technique, which feeds a minimal amount of heat into the liquid. Thus they had the usual cylindrical cavity with heater and thermometer (of carbon strip) at opposite ends; the whole hung vertically from a paramagnetic salt. The apparatus could, of course, be used for control measurements on pure He[4].

[1] K. R. Atkins and D. V. Osborne, *Phil. Mag.*, **41**:1078 (1950).

[2] de Klerk, Hudson, and Pellam, *Phys. Rev.*, **93**:28 (1954).

[3] D. V. Osborne, *Phil. Mag.*, **8**:301 (1956).

[4] J. C. King and H. A. Fairbank, *Phys. Rev.*, **93**:21 (1954).

Figure 68 shows some of their results together with a curve for pure He⁴ for comparison purposes.

The theory of these mixtures has been considered by Pomeranchuk[1] among others. In his derivation he makes certain assumptions in addition to the usual ones (see Chap. 4) which ignore irreversible effects and squares of velocity terms. First, he supposes that the He³ does not participate in the flow of the superfluid component—a good assumption, as we have seen. Second, he assumes that the solu-

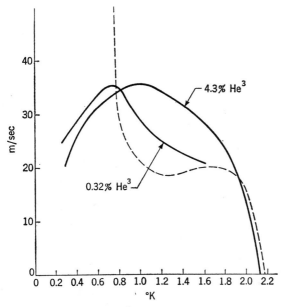

FIG. 68. Second sound velocity in two He³-He⁴ solutions. The dotted curve is for pure He⁴. (*King and H. A. Fairbank, 1954.*)

tions are dilute enough so that ideal-solution theory is applicable. His result is

$$u_2{}^2 = \frac{\rho_s}{\rho_{nm}} \frac{T}{C_m} \left[\left(S_0 + \frac{k\varepsilon}{m_4} \right)^2 + \frac{k\varepsilon}{m_4} C_m \right]$$

where S_0 = entropy of pure He⁴
$\quad C_m$ = specific heat of mixture
$\quad \varepsilon$ = molar fraction[2] of He³
$\quad m_4$ = mass of He⁴ atom
$\quad k$ = Boltzmann constant

[1] I. Pomeranchuk, *J. Exptl. Theoret. Phys. (U.S.S.R.),* **19**:42 (1949).
[2] $\varepsilon = n_3/n_4$ where n_3, n_4 are the number of atoms of He³ and He⁴, respectively, in 1 g of mixture.

The quantity ρ_{nm}, in the above formula, is not the same thing as the usual normal-component density; it will depend on ε in such a way that $\rho_{nm} \rightarrow \rho_n$ as ε vanishes, i.e.,

$$\rho_{nm} = \rho_{n0} + \rho_{ni}$$

where ρ_{n0} is our usual "ρ_n" for pure He^4 and ρ_{ni} is the contribution to "ρ_n" of the He^3 impurity. The precise form of ρ_{ni} will depend on the energy spectrum of the He^3 atoms dissolved in the superfluid. In lieu of an exceedingly difficult direct calculation Pomeranchuk assumes this to be of the form used, in similar circumstances, for rotons, i.e.,

$$E = E_0 + \frac{p^2}{2\mu}$$

where μ is, in this case, the "effective mass" of the He^3 atom when dissolved in the liquid. This number may, of course, be different from the true mass of the He^3 atom.

Under this condition, Pomeranchuk then shows that

$$\rho_{ni} = \frac{\rho\mu\varepsilon}{m_4}$$

where ρ is the (total) density of the solution.

Now our primary interest is the behavior of the second sound velocity for the dilute solution at low temperatures ($T < \sim 0.6°K$). Under these circumstances the dissolved He^3 atoms approach an ideal gas, and since also the phonon contribution is neglectably small, the specific heat of the mixture is due solely to the thermal excitation of the He^3 impurity (energy $\frac{1}{2}kT$ per degree of freedom per particle). Hence

$$C_m = \frac{3}{2} kn_4\varepsilon = \frac{3}{2} k \frac{1}{m_4} \varepsilon \qquad \text{per gram}$$

Then since $\rho_s \approx \rho$, the expression for u_2 reduces to

$$u_2{}^2 = \frac{5kT}{3\mu}$$

This is a quite different result from that for pure He^4 since

$$u_2 \rightarrow 0 \qquad T \rightarrow 0$$

and seems to be in agreement with King and Fairbank's results. In point of fact, these authors found that Pomeranchuk's expression is a good fit with the experimental values provided μ is made slightly temperature dependent, extrapolating to about twice the mass of the He^3

atom at 0°K. We note, in passing, that at the highest concentration used (4.3 per cent), the lowest temperature achieved ($\sim$0.3°K) was insufficient to split the solution into two phases.

The most direct way, of course, to measure the density ρ_{ni} is by means of an Andronikashvili pile-of-discs experiment. This was first done by Pellam[1] using a 4.4 mole per cent solution of He³. Such measurements were also reported by Dash and Taylor,[2] and Fig. 69 shows some results from both papers. According to King and Fairbank, the extrapolated value for the He³ effective mass is about $2m_3$ at 0°K. For a 4.4 per cent solution this is equivalent to about

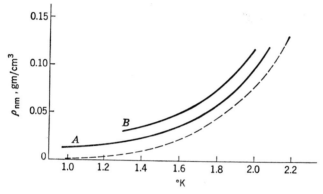

FIG. 69. Andronikashvili-type measurement in He³ solutions: Dotted curve, pure He⁴; curve A, 4.4 per cent He³ (*Pellam, 1955*); curve B, 10 per cent He³ (*Dash and Taylor*, 1957).

$\rho_{nm} \cong 0.01$ g/cm³, and we notice that Pellam's value seems to be approaching something like this number. Hence the two very different experiments appear to be in reasonably good concordance.

Feynman[3] has proposed a model to account for this effective mass of He³ dissolved in He⁴. In classical hydrodynamics it is well known that a sphere moving through a perfect fluid has an effective mass consisting of its proper mass plus half the mass of fluid displaced by the sphere. This arises because the sphere, in pushing the fluid aside, imparts kinetic energy to it which appears, therefore, as an added inertia imposed on the sphere. Feynman suggests that the He⁴ atoms are likewise pushed aside by the He³ atoms. He computes the flow using an approximate wave function and thence the kinetic energy

[1] J. R. Pellam, *Phys. Rev.*, **99**:1327 (1955).
[2] J. G. Dash and R. D. Taylor, *Phys. Rev.*, **107**:1228 (1957).
[3] R. P. Feynman, *Phys. Rev.*, **92**:262 (1954).

associated with it.   This gives $\mu = 1.9m_3$ in good agreement with the above.   This interesting idea really gives us a new type of mutual friction whereby the He^3 atoms (moving with the rotons and phonons) exert a drag upon the superfluid component.

SECOND SOUND AND PHASE SEPARATION

Elliott[1] and H. A. Fairbank have extended the second sound measurements to higher He^3 concentrations such that the phase separation occurs.   The pulse technique, with the cavity hung from

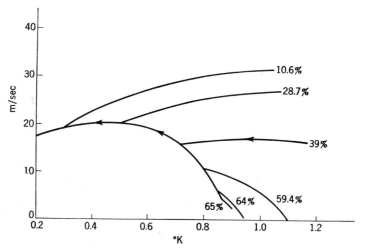

FIG. 70. Second sound velocity versus temperature for several He^3 solutions, show-ing the effect of phase separation.   (*Elliott and Fairbank*, 1958.)

the magnetic salt, was again employed, but the cylindrical cavity had its axis horizontal.   With the carbon resistance transducers per-pendicular to the axis and at either end of the cavity, these, upon phase separation, saw *two* liquids with the He^3-rich phase on top. Thus if both phases exhibited superfluidity, two signals traveling at different velocities (and therefore resolved in time) should be observed. A typical result is shown in Fig. 70.

These measurements, which extended from about 4 mole per cent He^3 up to 65 per cent and down to around 0.2°K, showed second sound to be found only in the dilute He^3 phase.   In Fig. 70 each per-centage attached to a curve is the concentration of He^3 in the unre-

[1] S. D. Elliott, Thesis, Yale, 1958.

frigerated gas mixture. Thus according to the Walters-Fairbank phase diagram the 39 per cent mixture, for example, would have a critical temperature of about 0.72°K, and this checks very well with the temperature at which phase splitting is seen to occur on the second sound diagram. As the temperature for this mixture is further decreased, the observed velocity points plot along the boundary curve toward the left, the velocity reaching, for example, 20 m/sec at about 0.53°K. At this temperature, according to the phase diagram, the 39 per cent mixture has a dilute phase containing about 23 per cent He³, the rich phase being around 78 per cent He³. Thus 20 m/sec should be the sound velocity at 0.53°K in a homogeneous mixture containing 23 per cent He³ provided the second sound is propagated in the dilute phase only. This is, in fact, very close to what is observed.

Now it is a property of the phase diagram (see Fig. 67) that, at any given temperature below the critical, the composition of the He³-poor phase (and the rich) is independent of the original composition of the unrefrigerated gas. This is precisely what the second sound results show, where we see that at a given temperature—for example, 0.6°K— the second sound velocities are identical for the 39, 59.4, and 64 per cent composition, namely, about 19.5 m/sec. This is so, of course, because at a given temperature the second sound velocity depends only on the liquid composition.

Since pure He³ is not, to the best of our knowledge, a superfluid, its second sound velocity would have to be zero at all temperatures down to 0°K. Hence very rich solutions would presumably have very low second sound velocities coupled with low λ points. This suggests that the boundary curve in Fig. 70 has to loop back on itself after touching 0.83°K, the highest allowed critical temperature. A glance at the Walters-Fairbank diagram shows that the highest concentration used in the second sound work (65 per cent) is just at the beginning of the He³-rich leg of the diagram. It would therefore clearly be of interest to extend the second sound measurements to higher concentrations so that some of the second sound could be measured outside the phase boundary.

Unfortunately, this does not appear very practical, as the authors point out. This is due to the fact that the second sound is, in general, highly attenuated at temperatures near the λ point, thus rendering the measurements uncertain, and it looks very much as though we should be operating very close to the λ point for concentrations beyond 65 per cent. This effect may also very well account for the failure to detect *two* signals, as was expected from the present experiment.

A useful byproduct of this work gives the λ temperature versus He³ concentration curve. This is achieved by extrapolating the velocity versus temperature graphs to zero velocity. Since such extrapolation is an accurate one and since second sound is a prime superfluid phenomenon, the result (Fig. 71) inspires considerable confidence. At the

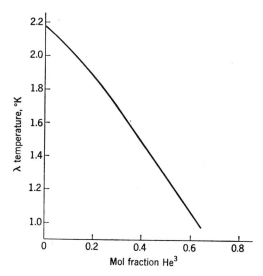

FIG. 71. The λ-point shift as a function of He³ concentration. (*Elliott and H. A. Fairbank, 1958.*)

moment it remains something of a question as to whether this curve and the He³-rich leg of the Walters-Fairbank diagram coincide or, alternatively, whether the former lies above the latter, as has been rather implied by our discussion above.

CHAPTER 8

Critical Velocities

ORIGIN OF THE IDEA OF A CRITICAL VELOCITY

It will be recalled that in Landau's theory a calculation was made for a "critical velocity" beyond which the superfluid lost its frictionless character. The result turned out to be very high, some 60 to 80 m/sec. We showed that a stream of superfluid moving through a pipe would need a velocity of this order to create rotons. The energy of the rotons would, under these circumstances, have to come from the kinetic energy of the moving stream. Hence this latter would slow down, and the net result would appear as a resistance to the stream; i.e., its frictionless character would disappear.

Actually the idea of such a critical velocity is older than Landau's theory and was first invoked by Daunt and Mendelssohn[1] to account for their observations of film flow out of beakers. This type of superfluid phenomenon (we have alluded to it in previous chapters) is quite easy to observe. If we take a small cylindrical vessel (axis vertical, closed at the bottom end and open at the other) and dip it part way into liquid helium II, the following effect takes place. The empty beaker slowly fills with liquid until the levels, inside and out, are identical. Conversely, if the beaker is raised so that the inner level is above the outer bath, the two levels again equalize. If, in fact, the

[1] J. G. Daunt and K. Mendelssohn, *Proc. Roy. Soc.* (*London*), **A170**:423, 439 (1939).

partly filled beaker is raised entirely clear of the bath, then liquid droplets form on the outside bottom and drip back into the bath!

The Oxford group of Rollin, Simon, Daunt, and Mendelssohn pretty nearly disposed of this subject prior to 1940—at least, since that time not much has been added to our knowledge with few exceptions. We know that the liquid transfer, in the above experiments, is due to a thin ($\sim 10^{-6}$ cm) film of liquid, part of which, at least, is mobile superfluid.

This "Rollin film" coats any surface brought in contact with He II and, in this respect, does not differ from a classical liquid, which wets surfaces by adhesion. It does, however, differ in the fact that the frictionless superfluid will move through the film either under the action of gravitational forces or because of the presence of temperature gradients.

In the isothermal beaker experiment, quoted above, the driving force is due to the gravitational potential difference between the two baths inside and outside the vessel, respectively, and the experiments show that the flow through the film is strictly independent of the difference in height between the two bulk liquid levels. The question at once arises, therefore, as to why with a finite gravitational potential difference the superfluid, being frictionless, does not assume an infinite flow velocity. Daunt and Mendelssohn answered this by supposing that, beyond a certain velocity, the superfluid suddenly loses its frictionless property.

Since the volume rate of influx of liquid into the beaker is readily measured, we can clearly compute this critical (i.e., maximum) velocity provided the thickness of the film is known. These authors made some crude measurements of this in their early work, but the best modern measurements of the total thickness of the film are due to Jackson and his students[1] using optical techniques. Combining these results, it turns out that the critical velocity in these films is about 70 cm/sec at the most, which is about two orders of magnitude below Landau's estimate. This optical approach shows that above the λ point a film of nearly the same thickness also exists; this has, of course, no flow properties since no superfluid component here exists.

In point of fact, it is not necessary to have bulk He II to form the film. A mobile film is found at temperatures below the λ point with unsaturated helium vapor, i.e., helium at a pressure less than the saturated vapor pressure at the temperature in question, so that no bulk liquid forms. Although a truly vast experimental effort has been expended on the Rollin film, the subject will not be pursued further

[1] A. C. Ham and L. C. Jackson, *Phil. Mag.*, **45**:1084 (1954), which gives references to previous work.

here since much of this effort, it must be admitted, has not paid off very significantly.

CRITICAL VELOCITIES WITH OSCILLATING SYSTEMS

What we might call "oscillation" experiments have played a key role in the study of superfluid phenomena—we have only to recall Andronikashvili's work to bring this fact home.   And critical velocity effects have repeatedly turned up in this type of experiment.

The earliest worker to make a study of this was Hallett,[1] using oscillating discs and spheres.   Figure 72 is a typical plot of the damp-

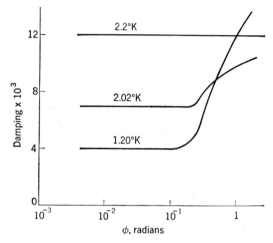

FIG. 72. Damping of a single disc in the He I and He II as a function of the amplitude of oscillation.   Period 11.0 sec.   (*Hallett*, 1952.)

ing suffered by the disc, in a normal-fluid viscosity experiment, as a function of the amplitude of the oscillations.   We see that (in He II) the damping, at all temperatures, is independent of amplitude only up to a certain critical amplitude.

Hallett extended these measurements to an Andronikashvili disc system and obtained curves very similar to those found for the single disc.   However, two extra points emerged.   Above φ_{crit}, the period of the system also increased, and just below the λ point the effective density computed from the observed period became equal to ρ, the total density; below the λ point it seemed to be approaching this for the shorter periods, i.e., higher speeds.

[1] Much of this work is conveniently summarized in the following paper: R. J. Donnelly and A. C. H. Hallett, *Ann. Phys.*, **3**:320 (1958).

Hallett's interpretation of this behavior was as follows. Below φ_{crit} only ρ_n follows the motion of the discs. At the value φ_{crit} an extra damping is observed which is accompanied by a motion of the superfluid, such that at temperatures near the λ point—or, in the case of lower temperatures, for high amplitudes of vibration—all the superfluid is entrained.[1]

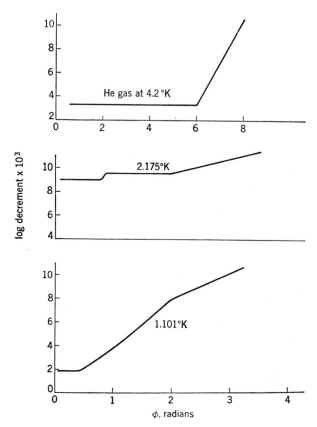

FIG. 73. Damping of an oscillating sphere in He gas and in He II. (*Benson and Hallett*, 1956.)

Hallett and Benson[2] made similar measurements for an oscillating sphere, which possesses a cleaner geometry than a disc system, albeit the velocity is variable over the sphere's surface. These measure-

[1] Recall that the period increases; hence the moment of inertia of the system must have increased. This could only be due to entrained superfluid.

[2] C. B. Benson and A. C. H. Hallett, *Can. J. Phys.*, **34**:668 (1956).

ments extended to somewhat higher amplitudes than the ones for the discs. The result (Fig. 73) showed a rather more complicated behavior with *two* critical velocities involved.

Finally, Donnelly and Penrose[1] performed an experiment on the decay of the oscillations of liquid helium in a U tube. Every student of physics has, at one time or another, doubtless stood before a mercury manometer and watched the levels oscillate. The above authors turned this everyday experience into a most interesting liquid-helium

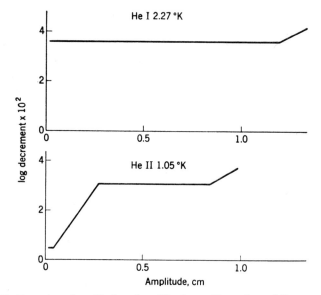

FIG. 74. Damping of oscillations in a U tube. (*Donnelly and Penrose*, 1956.)

experiment. Some results of this, which look similar to those for the sphere, are shown in Fig. 74.

The existence of *two* critical velocities (this is shown very clearly in the Donnelly-Penrose experiment) is somewhat clarified by the observations made with He gas (Fig. 73) and He I (Fig. 74) in which both show a critical velocity corresponding to the higher one in He II. In all cases the increase in decrement is linear with the amplitude, and this behavior, in turn, is consistent with a friction force proportional to the square of the velocity.

Now such a friction force is not typical of turbulence (i.e., vorticity) in a classical fluid; nevertheless, since both He gas and He I are classical fluids, we are tempted to ascribe the second critical velocity to some

[1] R. J. Donnelly and O. Penrose, *Phys. Rev.*, **103**:1137 (1956).

form of classical turbulence. The lower critical velocity, which, as we have seen, appears to occur at the onset of superfluid entrainment, is much more difficult to account for. It is pretty clearly connected with some sort of mutual friction, but to date no theoretical treatment exists which throws much light upon this. This is not very surprising since, even in classical fluids, "boundary layer theory" is an exceedingly awkward and difficult branch of theoretical mechanics. Donnelly and Hallett, in the review cited, offer some interesting views in this respect, for which their paper should be consulted.

KINEMATIC VISCOSITY OF He II

A matter which is fairly closely related to the above experiments concerns the kinematic viscosity of He II. In a classical fluid, this quantity is defined as the ratio of the viscosity coefficient to the fluid density. In He II, however, the question at once arises as to which density—ρ, ρ_n, or ρ_s—is involved, even assuming, as we have been doing, that the viscosity coefficient is that due to the normal component only.

In an attempt to answer this point Donnelly et al.[1] tried to measure this quantity directly. The apparatus consisted of a small beaker (similar to those used in film experiments) which could be set into rotation, at various speeds, about the vertical cylindrical axis. The beaker was partly filled with He II, and when at rest, the free surface was substantially a straight line. In steady rotation, however, this became a parabola (cf. Osborne's experiment). The experiment consisted of measuring the depth of the tip of the forming parabola (from the nonrotating free surface) as a function of time Z_t ($\Delta Z = Z_{t=\infty} - Z_t$).

For a classical fluid[2] the solution of the Navier-Stokes equation for this particular case gives

$$\Delta Z = A e^{-(\beta^2 \nu / a^2) t}$$

where A = a constant
$\beta = 3.83$ = first root of first-order Bessel
a = radius of beaker
ν = kinematic viscosity
t = time

The above expression is not exact but is a reasonably good approximation which, when used with ordinary fluids, gave good values for ν

---

[1] Donnelly, Chester, Walmsley, and Lane, *Phys. Rev.*, **102**:3 (1956).

[2] We recall that according to Osborne's experiment He II was classical at sufficiently high rotational speeds.

as compared with the usual method of determining η and ρ separately.

Figure 75 shows the experimental result. The experiment was found to give not a single plot for ΔZ versus t; rather, three different modes of behavior occurred (curves A, B, and C), and the one which any single run yielded was not under the control of the experimenters but occurred rather at random. Occasionally something much "worse" than the above pattern occurred, but in a large number of runs the above three were by far the most usual. Thus we may say

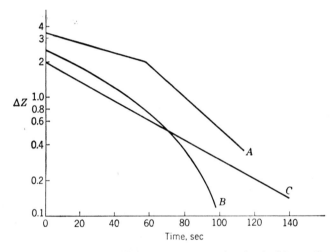

FIG. 75. Semilog plot of the meniscus height versus time in the kinematic-viscosity experiment. Temperature A and B, 1.5°K; C, 1.8°K. (*Donnelly*, 1956.)

that they, in all probability, represent the "stable modes" of the system.

Clearly, the only one of the three to which the above analysis applied was curve C, which also happened to be the one most frequently observed.[1] Comparing this with the above formula showed that ν decreased slightly from about 2.4 $\times$ 10^{-4} cm^2/sec at 1.1°K to 1.4 $\times$ 10^{-4} cm^2/sec at 2.1°K. Check measurements in He I (at 2.25°K) yielded a value of 2.2 $\times$ 10^{-4} cm^2/sec, whereas that computed from the known viscosity coefficient and density of He I at this temperature gave 1.7 $\times$ 10^{-4} cm^2/sec. The measurement, accordingly, was not a very accurate one. Nevertheless, it showed very clearly that the

[1] Curve B, for instance, always occurred when a small "tip" appeared at the bottom of the forming parabola. This mode (also A) led to the eventual formation of a vortex rather than a "solid body" parabola (see Chap. 6).

density involved in the kinematic viscosity of He II was the total density ρ.[1] In other words, at the high speeds of this experiment ($\sim$15 rps) the superfluid was totally entrained.

Similar estimates of ν can be made from the data for the oscillating-sphere and U-tube experiments, and these give values which are about the same as the above. It is interesting to note that Onsager[2] has pointed out that the kinematic viscosity of He II has the same magnitude and dimensions as the ratio $\hbar/m$.

TWO-FLUID HYDRODYNAMICS

The Navier-Stokes equation, which is the correct equation of motion of a classical viscous fluid, has been employed by us several times. At the risk of being repetitious, we will again state it:

$$\rho \frac{D\mathbf{v}}{Dt} = \rho \left[\frac{\partial \mathbf{v}}{\partial t} + (\mathbf{v} \cdot \nabla)\mathbf{v} \right] = -\nabla P + \eta \left[\tfrac{4}{3}\nabla(\nabla \cdot \mathbf{v}) - \nabla \times \nabla \times \mathbf{v} \right] + \mathbf{F}$$

Here $\mathbf{F}$ is an external force per unit volume, which in the future, for the sake of simplicity, we shall generally assume to be zero. In the case of He II we presumably need two such equations, one for each component, and the question arises as to what form they should take. We must suppose that each would be founded on the above, with terms added and subtracted to take into account some special properties (fountain effect, for example) not present in any classical liquid. On some particulars, however, such as mutual friction, we do not have any clear picture as to what this term (or terms) should look like. Hence, at the present writing, the "ultimate" formulation of the two-fluid equations has not been approached.

Some points, of course, are reasonably established. Thus the superfluid viscosity term will not be present; also the liquid is reasonably incompressible and so $\nabla \cdot \mathbf{v} = 0$. Further, the fountain effect is well established. Referring to our prior discussion (Chap. 4) of the second sound, we showed that

$$\rho_n \dot{\mathbf{v}}_n = -\rho_s S \nabla T$$

---

[1] At 1.1°K, for instance, if we assumed that ρ_n was the correct density to use, then the normal-component viscosity resulting from the measured value of ν would be 0.6 micropoise, which is less than that observed with an oscillating disc by a factor of about 50.

[2] L. Onsager, *Proc. Intern. Conf. Theoret. Phys. Kyoto and Tokyo, Japan*, 1953, p. 877.

This is the fountain effect action-reaction force on the two fluids. Hence, as a first try, our two equations might look like this:

$$\rho_n \frac{D\mathbf{v}_n}{Dt} = - \frac{\rho_n}{\rho} \nabla P - \rho_s S \nabla T + \eta \nabla^2 \mathbf{v}_n \tag{1}$$

$$\rho_s \frac{D\mathbf{v}_s}{Dt} = - \frac{\rho_s}{\rho} \nabla P + \rho_s S \nabla T \tag{2}$$

We note that when $\rho_s \to 0$ and hence $\rho_n \to \rho$ we get the classical Navier-Stokes equation as we should. We realize that this pair of equations is certainly incomplete from the standpoint of many experiments. One obvious lack, as stated, is that they contain no mutual-friction terms, $F_{sn}(v_s, v_n)$.

Landau, in his celebrated 1941 paper, deduced the two-fluid hydrodynamic equations by postulating a form of the Gibbs function in the two-fluid. This leads to the above equations with the addition of another term, namely,

$$\frac{\rho_s \rho_n}{2\rho} \nabla (v_s - v_n)^2$$

which vanishes at both the λ point and absolute zero. It is not, as has sometimes been supposed, a mutual-friction term; its physical makeup is rather more in the nature of a Bernoulli-pressure term when the two fluids are in relative motion to each other.

Additionally, the Landau criterion $\nabla \times \mathbf{v}_s = 0$ does not appear in the above formulation. Thus if, for simplicity, we agree to stick to small velocities of the superfluid so that $(\mathbf{v} \cdot \nabla)\mathbf{v}$ is neglectable and also ignore mutual-friction and external forces, then by taking the curl of both sides of Eq. (2) we get

$$\rho_s \frac{\partial}{\partial t} (\nabla \times \mathbf{v}_s) = - \frac{\rho_s}{\rho} \nabla \times (\nabla P) + \rho_s S \nabla \times (\nabla T)$$

that is,

$$\frac{\partial}{\partial t} (\nabla \times \mathbf{v}_s) = 0$$

which means that $\nabla \times \mathbf{v}_s = $ a constant, which is by no means the same thing as the Landau criterion. It simply means that in a perfect fluid, vorticity once created will persist for all time, which is an old and famous result.

Despite all these imperfections, these equations have been useful. They will (as Landau and Tisza originally showed) correctly predict the second sound phenomenon to first approximation, i.e., without predicting an attenuation for the wave. They do not, however, show anything like a critical velocity and would not do so with any simple mutual-friction term. To account for such, we need something quite different. All this is another way of saying that a classical formulation of the helium problem is insufficient.

ISOTHERMAL FLOW IN NARROW CHANNELS

We have mentioned that the flow of superfluid through the Rollin film is strictly independent of pressure head. This is an extreme example of flow through a "narrow channel," the film thick-

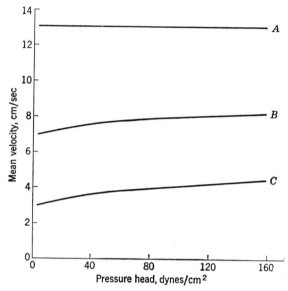

FIG. 76. Superfluid flow through narrow channels at 1.2°K. Channel widths: A, 0.12 μ; B, 0.8 μ; C, 3.9 μ. (*Atkins*, 1952.)

ness being less than 200 A. Many attempts have been made to produce narrow mechanical channels, for example, by pressing optically flat plates together or by packing fine tubes with some powder such as jeweler's rouge. Neither of these processes produces a clean geometry— such channels are never very uniform, especially the latter. And to what extent this fact influences the results is a moot question.

It is easy to study the flow through such channels by allowing them to connect two baths at different levels (see, for instance, Kapitza's fountain-effect apparatus). The results, in general, look something like Fig. 76, which is taken from a paper by Atkins.[1] We see that,

[1] K. R. Atkins, *Phil. Mag. Suppl.*, **1**:169 (1952).

depending on the width of the channel, the flow is different. For the narrowest channel which can be contrived ($\sim$0.1 μ) the result, however, agrees with the situation in the film,[1] as far as dependence on pressure head is concerned. But we see that the critical velocity is some five times smaller. It is also apparent that, in general, as the channel width increases, the critical velocity diminishes.

FEYNMAN'S EXPLANATION

We recall that, in the oscillating-sphere experiments in the (classical) helium gas, what looked like a critical velocity occurred at a sufficiently large amplitude. This was ascribed to the onset of turbulence, i.e., where the fluid pattern changed from laminar flow to eddies or vortex motions. The place where this happens, in the classical fluid, is dependent on the kinematic viscosity of the fluid in question. Now in the case of the superfluid we have seen that vortex motions, probably quantized, can occur, and Feynman[2] has suggested that we look for critical velocities in terms of these. In order to see where this idea leads and following Feynman, we make an order-of-magnitude calculation as follows.

Consider a narrow channel (as between two flat plates) through which superfluid is flowing in the x direction. Let the width of the channel be d (z direction), and we take unit depth of it (y direction). The channel enters, as is the case in the experiments, into a large reservoir of liquid.

As always, the fluid (being frictionless) would reach infinite velocities under a finite pressure head unless checked by some mechanism. The mechanism here is the formation of quantized vortices which possess self-energy; by taking this energy from the kinetic energy of the stream, they slow it down and so impose a resistance which limits its speed to critical. We have no sure knowledge as to how these vortices are formed or, for that matter, where. It may be at the walls of the slit or possibly where the fluid exits into the bath. In any event, these lines, with their axes parallel to the y direction, are continually ejected into the bath. If we call the distance between adjacent lines (in the x direction) x and their number per unit distance in this direction n and apply Stokes' theorem over a contour of unit length in the x direction in the fluid stream with a return outside the stream, then

[1] As long as the channel width is less than about 10^{-3} cm, the normal-component flow, because of its viscosity, is negligible.

[2] R. P. Feynman, "Progress in Low Temperature Physics," vol. 1, p. 45, Interscience Publishers, Inc., New York, 1955.

$$v1 = \frac{h}{m} n \qquad n = \frac{1}{x}$$

that is,
$$v = \frac{h}{m}\frac{1}{x}$$

Now the energy of each line is[1]

$$\pi\rho \left(\frac{\hbar}{m}\right)^2 \ln \frac{d}{a}$$

and in 1 sec, when the fluid goes a distance v, there will be created v/x lines/sec. Hence the energy devoted to vortex creation per second will be

$$\frac{v}{x} \pi\rho \left(\frac{\hbar}{m}\right)^2 \ln \frac{d}{a} = \frac{v^2 \pi\rho \left(\frac{\hbar}{m}\right)^2 \ln \frac{d}{a}}{h/m}$$

Now the energy per unit volume of the stream is $\rho v^2/2$, and in our geometry the stream occupies a volume vd/sec, so that if we call v_c the critical velocity, this latter energy will be just sufficient to create the above vortices, i.e.,

$$\frac{v_c^2 \pi\rho(\hbar/m)^2 \ln\,(d/a)}{h/m} = \frac{\rho v_c^2}{2} v_c d$$

that is,
$$v_c d = \frac{\hbar}{m} \ln \frac{d}{a}$$

Thus for $d = 0.1\ \mu$ and assuming the line core $a \cong 3$ A, we get

$$v_c \cong 100 \text{ cm/sec}$$

Considering the very crude nature of the computation, the result is not too bad—it is about seven times the experimental result (Fig. 76), certainly far better than the estimate of 80 m/sec which results from Landau's theory. Further, it is in the right direction to account for the fact that the critical velocity diminishes as the slit width increases. Atkins[2] has assembled the results of a good number of experiments dealing with critical velocities in the film and in narrow channels, and we reproduce his data in Fig. 77. It is seen that over a wide range of channel widths the critical velocity is a function of the kind required by Feynman's vortex picture.

The critical velocities involved in the "acceleration" experiments (oscillating-sphere, U-tube, etc.) are a good deal less than this—often

[1] See footnote page 133.

[2] K. R. Atkins, "Liquid Helium," p. 200, Cambridge University Press, New York, 1959.

as low as 0.1 cm/sec.[1]   There is, of course, some difference in the
mechanisms of the two kinds of experiments.   In the case of the steady
flow through slits, the critical velocity is the one which produces
enough energy in the stream to create vorticity and so limit any
further increase in this velocity.   In the acceleration experiments, on
the other hand, we observe the velocity of the system at which it just
commences to force the superfluid into motion.   This, however, is not
a very fundamental difference; in both instances it is the velocity of
the superfluid relative to the solid boundary which counts.   And in

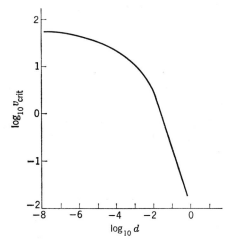

FIG. 77. Dependence of the critical flow velocity v_{crit} on the channel width d in cgs
units.   (*Atkins*, 1959.)

the latter case the creation of vortex lines is the same thing as forcing
the superfluid into motion from an initial state of rest.

The experiment of Craig and Pellam (superfluid wind tunnel), which
we discussed in Chap. 6, is a good example of a critical-velocity effect.
Here the critical velocity was very distinct (0.6 cm/sec), marking the
boundary between purely frictionless flow and some form of induced
turbulence in the superfluid.   In discussing experiments of this kind,
it is not strictly necessary to infer that below the critical velocity the
superfluid flow is potential (i.e., $\nabla \times \mathbf{v}_s = 0$).   It might be that below
critical the viscosity of the superfluid is vanishingly small, in which
case, as we showed previously, $\nabla \times \mathbf{v}_s = $ a constant.   The role of the
critical velocity would then be to make the viscosity suddenly finite.

[1] This is the maximum velocity of the oscillating system corresponding to the
first critical amplitude.

As a matter of fact no experiment, to date, *clearly* distinguishes between these two possibilities. Perhaps the best one—and this is very incomplete—is due to Reynolds, Good, and Schultis[1] in which they measured the torque exerted on a right cylinder (axis vertical) which makes torsion pendulum oscillations in He II. Assuming $\nabla \times v_s = 0$, the period of the system can be computed, since the velocity potential obeys Laplace's equation. This is the same problem as computing the effective mass of the sphere moving through a perfect fluid. The result could then be compared with the experiment, and it was found that at sufficiently low temperatures where ρ_n is becoming small, the agreement was not too bad.

MUTUAL FRICTION AND CRITICAL VELOCITY

As originally enunciated by Gorter and Mellink,[2] the mutual-friction force (per unit volume) between the two fluids in relative linear motion (i.e., barring the special case of rotation) was

$$F_{sn} = A\rho_s\rho_n(|v_s - v_n| - v_0)^3 \qquad v_0 \sim 1 \text{ cm/sec}$$

Here A is an empirical constant. The proposal was made, as we previously stated, to account for anomalies in the flow of heat through He II confined to narrow channels.

Now in Hallett's work with oscillating discs we make use of the two-fluid hydrodynamic equations (1) and (2) *without* the mutual-friction term, which, under the usual restrictions of small velocities, gives

$$\rho_n \frac{\partial v_n}{\partial t} = \eta\nabla^2 v_n$$
$$v_s = 0$$

These equations permit us to find, via the experiments, η (the viscosity of the normal fluid) provided ρ_n is known, and the results of this are always accepted.

But if we add the mutual-friction term to the above equation, the result is naturally different—it turns out that the damping should increase as the velocity increases. As we recall, the experiments show no such effect until a critical amplitude (i.e., velocity) is reached, after which point they do. Hence the disc experiments suggest that the mutual friction and critical velocity are interdependent in the sense that the former comes into play only after the latter is reached.

[1] J. M. Reynolds, B. J. Good, and W. J. Schultis, Proceedings Madison Conference, p. 21, 1958.

[2] C. J. Gorter and J. H. Mellink, *Physica*, 15:285 (1949).

Vinen[1] has reported an interesting experiment in which he uses second sound as a tool to investigate mutual friction set up when the two fluids move relative to one another because of a thermal gradient. As has been mentioned, a mutual-friction term, of whatever form, introduced into the hydrodynamic equations will lead to a spatial attenuation of the second sound wave.   In this experiment the helium is confined in a long pipe of rectangular cross section, along which a thermal gradient may be imposed.   At opposite ends of the longer axis of the cross section the pipe contains a second sound heater and

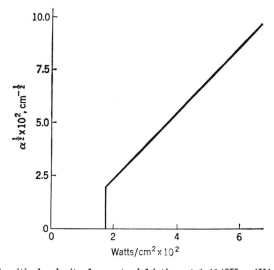

FIG. 78. A critical velocity for mutual friction at 1.414°K.   (*Vinen*, 1957.)

thermometer.   At a given frequency, therefore, this cavity is resonant for standing second sound waves, and, as in the similar case of the rotational experiments, the width of the resonance curve is a measure of the dissipation or attenuation.

Figure 78 shows a plot of the quantity $\alpha^{1/2}$, where α is the linear attenuation constant of the second sound, versus the steady heat current density (watts per square centimeter) produced by the temperature gradient along the pipe, i.e., at right angles to the second sound propagation.   These heat currents were such that the relative velocity $(v_s - v_n)$ ranged from about 1 to 15 cm/sec.   We see that there is a very distinct critical velocity for the mutual friction, which occurs at a relative velocity $(v_s - v_n)$ of approximately 0.6 cm/sec.   However, *outside* the temperature range 1.35 to 1.45°K the experiment shows no

[1] W. F. Vinen, *Proc. Roy. Soc. (London)*, **A240**:114 (1957).

critical velocity.   This might mean either that it is nonexistent or else that it has too low a value, so that the method is not sufficiently sensitive here to detect any mutual friction.[1]

However this may be, the experiment shows very clearly that, when mutual friction does set in, the attenuation coefficient is proportional to the square of the steady heat current density.   This fact permits us to construct a function for F_{sn}.   If we call the velocity of the normal component in the steady heat current V_n, then

$$W = \rho S V_n T$$

Further, if we add to the hydrodynamical equations (1) and (2) a mutual-friction term linear in $(v_s - v_n)$ which we can call

$$F_{sn} = G(\mathbf{v}_s - \mathbf{v}_n)$$

where $G = (\rho_s \rho_n/\rho) f(V_n)$, it is not difficult to show that the resulting wave equation for the entropy contains a term $f(V_n)(\partial S/\partial t)$.[2]   Further, this equation has a solution of the form

$$S = S_0 e^{i(kx - \omega_0 t)}$$

where $$k = k_0 \left[1 + i \frac{f(V_n)}{\omega_0} \right]^{\frac{1}{2}} \cong k_0 \left[1 + i \frac{f(V_n)}{2\omega_0} \right]$$

to a first approximation.

This means that the wave has an attenuation with a constant

$$\alpha = \frac{f(V_n)}{2u_2}$$

Since the experiment requires $\alpha \propto W^2$, this suggests

$$f(V_n) = V_n^2 = \frac{W^2}{\rho^2 S^2 T^2}$$

so that the experiments are accounted for by a mutual-friction term of the form

$$\mathbf{F}_{sn} = A(W - W_0)^2 (\mathbf{v}_s - \mathbf{v}_n)$$

where W_0 is the heat current density at the critical velocity.

[1] This measured attenuation is, of course, a function of $(v_s - v_n)$, and the sensitivity of the apparatus was such that it could not measure an attenuation below $v_s - v_n \cong 0.2$ cm/sec.

[2] The equation now reads

$$\frac{\partial^2 S}{\partial t^2} + f(V_n) \frac{\partial S}{\partial t} - \frac{S^2 T}{C} \frac{\rho_s}{\rho_n} \frac{\partial^2 S}{\partial x^2} = 0$$

in the one-dimensional case.

In a second paper Vinen[1] has reported some interesting transient effects connected with this experiment. It was found, for example, that when a steady heat current greater than critical (i.e., greater than W_0) was switched on, in initially undisturbed helium, the coefficient G rose to an equilibrium value only after a delay time of the order of 1 sec. Conversely, when the heat current was suddenly switched off, it took something like 30 sec for G to vanish. Vinen presents plausible arguments which suggest that these time effects are caused by the growth or decay of turbulence in the superfluid. This he envisages as a complex tangled array of vortex lines.

[1] W. F. Vinen, *op. cit.*, p. 128.

CHAPTER 9

Superconductivity

NATURE OF THE EFFECT

The reader who has had the patience to reach this point may also have reached the conclusion that superflow is a property of one unique gas out of the hundred or so chemical elements. This, however, would be untrue since there is another gas which exhibits it under certain circumstances, namely, the dense gas formed by the conduction electrons in some metals. In fact, this superfluid phenomenon was discovered much earlier than that in liquid helium and was called by its discoverer, Kamerlingh Onnes, "supra" conductivity —in modern parlance, superconductivity.

Quite soon after Onnes succeeded in liquefying helium in 1908 and thus producing a low-temperature range hitherto unavailable, he had occasion to measure the electrical resistivity of a wire of mercury. This thread of mercury, frozen in a glass capillary, was, by modern standards, none too pure. Nevertheless, the resistivity, after being nearly temperature independent from around $14°K$ down, suddenly, near $4°K$, "lost" its resistance; i.e., it became unmeasurably small, perhaps zero. By suddenly is meant that the resistance dropped from a finite to a zero value in a small temperature interval—perhaps $\frac{1}{10}°K$. And the resistance remained vanishingly small at all reachable lower temperatures below this transition.

Not very much later (around 1912) it was found that the vanishing resistance could be restored to a finite value by applying a magnetic field of suitable ("critical") value along the wire's axis. This critical field is a function of temperature such that its value increases as the temperature gap measured from the transition temperature increases. Figure 79 shows a typical modern result, and this plot is called a threshold field curve. This threshold curve makes a boundary; outside it the resistance is always finite, and inside it is vanishingly small. It has therefore every appearance of marking the boundary of some sort of phase transition.

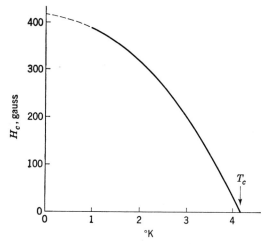

FIG. 79. The magnetic threshold curve for superconducting mercury. The curve must have zero slope at 0°K because entropy differences between the two phases must vanish there. Only at points *inside* this boundary is the metal superconducting. The curve is almost, but not exactly, parabolic.

In the 50 years since the discovery, a large number of additional metallic elements, some 22 in number, have been found to be superconductors. They differ from one another in that they have different transition temperatures and magnitudes of threshold fields. Alloys of these metals are always new superconductors, and cases have been found wherein binary alloys of two nonsuperconductors are superconducting (e.g., Au_2Bi).

There is no obvious correlation between the crystal-lattice structure of the various superconductors—these are widely diversified. On the other hand, "white" tin (tetragonal lattice) is a superconductor, whereas "gray" tin (diamond lattice) is not. Curiously, the metals copper and silver, which we think of as the best electrical conductors, in the usual sense, are not superconductors down to the lowest temperatures (∼20 millidegrees K) so far investigated. This is true also for the ferromagnetics iron, nickel, and cobalt.

Very soon after the discovery, Onnes set about determining whether the resistance in the superphase was really zero and not merely smaller than his (and our) rather crude resistivity measurements could detect. To this end he performed a number of really ingenious experiments, and perhaps the best of them was the superconducting ring. In this he suspended a small toroidal ring of Pb by means of a torsion fiber, the ring's plane being vertical. He then applied a magnetic field perpendicular to the ring's plane, using an external magnet. The ring was next cooled down below its transition temperature ($\sim 7°$K for Pb) and the field removed. As soon as the decaying field fell below critical, at the temperature of the experiment, the ring became superconducting, whence further reduction of the field induced a persistent current around the ring by Faraday induction.

Now a ring of area A carrying a current i is equivalent to a small magnet of moment $\mu = iA$.

If now a uniform magnetic field H_0[1] whose value is less than critical is applied at right angles to the normal to the ring's plane, the latter will experience a torque and turn through an angle φ such that

$$k\varphi = iAH_0 \cos \varphi$$

Clearly, the angle φ will remain constant as long as the current i does so. Since changes in φ can be measured optically with great precision, the method is a very sensitive one. The decay of current in a ring whose resistance is R and inductance L is

$$i = i_0 e^{-(R/L)t}$$

In Onnes's experiment t was several hours and L readily computable from the ring's dimensions. Hence an upper limit for R could be found which turned out to be about $10^{-12} R_0$, wherein R_0 was the ring's resistance at $0°$C. Just *above* the transition the resistance of the ring would measure typically $10^{-2} R_0$. Hence the transition has reduced the resistance by a factor of at least 10^{10}!

The experiment has been repeated in recent years with longer times of duration, and the upper limit has been further reduced to around $10^{-20} R_0$. By comparison, this ratio for the purest single crystal of copper at helium temperatures is about $10^{-9} R_0$. Thus if the resistance in a superconductor is zero, as it certainly appears to be, the potential difference in the presence of the persistent current is likewise zero, which means that the electric field in the specimen is zero. This is often called the Onnes effect.

[1] He used a second lead ring, perpendicular to the first, with a supercurrent in it for this purpose.

The clear point which emerges from all this is that we are able to set up a frictionless flow in the electron liquid, that is to say, one with no pressure head (potential difference). The "critical velocity" is, of course, the magnetic threshold; when the electron current becomes great enough to produce a field which exceeds this, the resistance becomes normal again (Silsbee effect) and limits the flow.

All this is very reminiscent of the He II problem, and we are tempted to handle it in the same way. That is to say, in a superconductor, a certain fraction of the conduction electrons become superfluid with no viscosity. The transition temperature corresponds to the λ point, and the superfluid fraction smoothly increases as the temperature is reduced below it. We can, in fact, write down a Navier-Stokes equation for the electron liquid, dropping out the viscosity terms for the superfluid part. However, since we are dealing with electric and magnetic fields and since the particles in this liquid carry charge, there are additional force terms. In the presence of fields E and H the forces per unit volume will be

$$\frac{\rho e}{m}\left[\mathbf{E} + \frac{1}{c}\left(\mathbf{v} \times \mathbf{H}\right)\right]$$

Now $\quad \rho\dfrac{D\mathbf{v}}{Dt} = \rho\dfrac{\partial \mathbf{v}}{\partial t} + \rho(\mathbf{v}\cdot\nabla)\mathbf{v} = \rho\dfrac{\partial \mathbf{v}}{\partial t} + \rho\nabla\left(\dfrac{v^2}{2}\right) - \rho(\mathbf{v}\times\nabla\times\mathbf{v})$

and $\quad \rho\dfrac{D\mathbf{v}}{Dt} = \rho\dfrac{e}{m}\left[\mathbf{E} + \dfrac{1}{c}\left(\mathbf{v}\times\mathbf{H}\right)\right]$

Hence $\quad \dfrac{\partial \mathbf{v}}{\partial t} + \nabla\left(\dfrac{v^2}{2}\right) - \dfrac{\mathbf{E}e}{m} = \left[\mathbf{v}\times\left(\nabla\times\mathbf{v} + \dfrac{e\mathbf{H}}{mc}\right)\right]$

This equation, which is purely classical and has many solutions, is, for instance, satisfied by $E = 0 \qquad v = 0 \qquad H = $ constant. But it turns out, as we shall see, that an actual superconductor does not behave in this manner.

MEISSNER EFFECT

In 1933 Meissner and Ochsenfeld[1] measured the magnetic susceptibility of a superconductor in fields less than critical. And the result was not at all in accordance with the classical expectation. We shall not discuss the actual experiment as performed by these authors— rather, we shall idealize it somewhat without, however, any loss of rigor. By this procedure we shall hope to make the nature of the discovery rather clearer.

[1] W. Meissner and R. Ochsenfeld, *Naturwissenschaften*, **21**:787 (1933).

Imagine a long thin cylinder of superconducting metal in a cryostat, with a uniform magnetic field whose direction is along the cylinder's axis and whose magnitude is under the control of the operator. Let the temperature be set somewhat below the transition and then the field increased from zero to some value beyond critical and thence reduced to zero again. Let us observe the intensity of magnetization (I) in the sample by observing its magnetic susceptibility with some standard technique. What, classically, would we be led to expect? In the sample, according to Maxwell, we should have

$$\nabla \times \mathbf{E} = -\frac{1}{c}\frac{\partial \mathbf{B}}{\partial t}$$
$$\mathbf{B} = \mathbf{H} + 4\pi \mathbf{I}$$

But, since the sample is superconducting, $E = 0$ and so $B =$ constant in time. This means that since the field inside the sample (B) was zero to begin with, it must remain so until the sample loses its superconductivity when $H = H_c$.

Hence $I = -\dfrac{H}{4\pi}$ $0 \lessgtr H \lessgtr H_c$ $I \cong 0$ $H > H_c$†

Next, as said, we relax the field. When it again reaches H_c, E will once more have to vanish and so, from this time on, $B = H_c$, whence

$$I = \frac{H_c - H}{4\pi} \qquad H < H_c$$

This result is plotted in Fig. 80a. We see, then, that after this cycle the specimen is left with a "frozen in" magnetic moment (per unit volume) of amount $+H_c/4\pi$; our specimen has become and will behave like a permanent magnet. The physical reason is, of course, clear—we have induced a persistent current whose magnetic field looks like a dipole.

The early workers, immersed in classical physics, considered this result to be so self-evident that it took nearly 20 years before anyone thought it worthwhile to have a look experimentally. When Meissner and Ochsenfeld did so, they found a very different result, shown typically in Fig. 80b.

As mentioned, Meissner and Ochsenfeld did not do the experiment this way. They actually used a spherical sample and measured the field distribution around its surface by means of flip coils. But the result was precisely as we have described, extrapolated to the simpler

† The magnetic susceptibility of any superconductor in the normal state is very small, of the order of 10^{-6} emu/gm.

geometry. This, however, was not all they found. They discovered
that the flux distribution around the sphere when it was cooled below
the superconducting transition in a time-invariant field of magnitude
less than critical was quite accurately that for a body in which $B = 0$!
Said differently, it is possible to induce currents in the specimen *by a
time-invariant* magnetic field merely by lowering the temperature.
This behavior is completely at variance with Maxwell's classical equa-

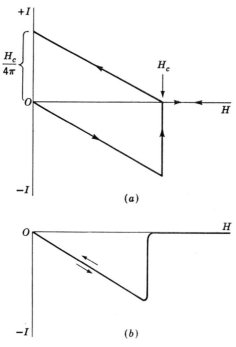

FIG. 80. (a) Magnetization curve for a superconducting wire according to classical
electrodynamics; (b) the experimental value for a "wire" in the form of a thin
evaporated film of Sn. (*Lock*, 1951.)

tion curl $\mathbf{E} = -(1/c)\dot{\mathbf{B}}$ and must, therefore, be a quantum effect
exhibited on a macroscopic scale.

Thus our picture is that when we cool our sample below the transition in a field less than critical, the lines of force are ejected from the
body of the specimen. Said differently, currents are induced whose
field annuls that originally threading the specimen. For a long wire
the susceptibility for $B = 0$, therefore, becomes

$$\chi = \frac{I}{H} = -\frac{1}{4\pi}$$

which is a huge diamagnetic value ("perfect diamagnetism") compared to ordinary para- or diamagnetics.[1]

F. AND H. LONDON'S PROPOSAL

With the discovery of the Meissner effect, the course for the quantum theoreticians was charted—explain the effect and its practical applications will follow. The problem proved to be one of the most intractable in the history of physics, and it was not until 1957 that Bardeen, Cooper, and Schrieffer came up with what certainly looks like the solution. However, prior to this, the Londons made important contributions to the problem.[2]

It is apparent that a superconductor, analogous to He II, has a two-fluid character. In other words, there are *two* conduction-current densities which we may call J_n and J_s. They are both, of course, electronic but, we guess, the energy states differ. $J_n = \sigma E$ is the ordinary ohmic current found in the normal state of the metal (i.e., outside the threshold curve) and perhaps also in the superconducting region. J_s, on the other hand, is to be found only inside the boundary of the threshold curve. In other words, J_n is the classical component (normal component) and J_s is the superfluid. J_n will therefore obey Maxwell's equations and in some respects so will J_s, e.g., as far as the production of magnetic fields is concerned. However, J_s is very unclassical in other respects (e.g., Meissner effect) and will obey some new, purely quantum, equation.

The London proposals for the electrodynamics of the superconductor reflect all this and are as follows:[3]

$$\nabla \times \mathbf{E} = -\frac{1}{c}\dot{\mathbf{H}} \tag{1}$$

$$\nabla \times \mathbf{H} = \frac{4\pi}{c}(\mathbf{J}_n + \mathbf{J}_s) \tag{2}$$

$$\nabla \times \lambda\mathbf{J}_s = -\mathbf{H} \tag{3}$$

$$\nabla \cdot \mathbf{H} = 0 \tag{4}$$

$$\nabla \cdot \mathbf{J}_n = \nabla \cdot \mathbf{J}_s = 0 \tag{5}$$

[1] For other regular shapes the relation is

$$B = H + 4\pi(1 - n)I$$

where $n = \frac{1}{3}$ for a sphere. $4\pi n$ is called the demagnetizing or shape factor. Thus, for a sphere $\chi = -3/8\pi$.

[2] A full account is given in F. London, "Superfluids," John Wiley & Sons, Inc., New York, 1950, vol. I.

[3] Gaussian units. Displacement currents are omitted in this "low frequency" discussion.

Here λ is a characteristic constant different for different superconductors. The only one of these equations which is unfamiliar to us is
(3)—this is the London postulate.   We will postpone the background
thinking which led to it and consider first the implications of the
above set.

Ignoring the normal current J_n as not of immediate interest and
taking the curl of both sides of (2), we have

$$\nabla \times \nabla \times \mathbf{H} = \nabla\nabla \cdot \mathbf{H} - \nabla^2\mathbf{H} = \frac{4\pi}{c} \nabla \times \mathbf{J}_s$$

and using (3) to (5), we get finally

$$\nabla^2\mathbf{H} = \frac{4\pi}{\lambda c} \mathbf{H} \tag{6}$$

And, in a similar manner,

$$\nabla^2\mathbf{J}_s = \frac{4\pi}{\lambda c} \mathbf{J}_s \tag{7}$$

From both these equations it is clear that H (or J_s) decreases exponentially from its surface value as we penetrate into a superconductor.
Thus if we consider for instance a semi-infinite slab of superconductor
in the xy plane with z positive into the metal and H_0, at the outside
surface, uniform and parallel to the x direction, then

$$H_x = H_0 e^{-\sqrt{4\pi/\lambda c}\, z}$$

with a similar expression for J_s. As a consequence of (2) we note
that, under these circumstances, J_s flows in the y direction. As is
usual for exponential functions, we define a "penetration depth" δ
such that

$$H_x = H_0 e^{-1} \quad \text{when} \quad z = \delta$$

(Compare the similar situation for viscous waves in a classical fluid.)
This yields

$$\delta = \sqrt{\frac{\lambda c}{4\pi}}$$

It is clear, therefore, that the field inside the metal decreases very
rapidly to zero provided δ, and hence the characteristic parameter λ,
is a small quantity, and this would then agree pretty closely with
Meissner's result. And equally clear would be the fact that the
supercurrents are surface currents. Hence everything now depends

on deducing some number for λ; this, of course, we might do experimentally, but a theoretical estimate would be useful.

THE ACCELERATED CURRENT

There is no way of deducing Eq. (3) classically; if it is true at all, it is certainly a matter for quantum mechanics. We can, however, gain a better insight into the nature of the parameter λ by the following considerations.

The Onnes-ring experiment has shown that the electron flow forming the supercurrent is frictionless. If we somehow apply a steady electric field E to such an array of superelectrons, they will all be accelerated in the field direction, i.e.,

$$m\dot{\mathbf{v}} = \mathbf{E}e$$

The current density J_s of such a group (n_s per unit volume) is

$$\mathbf{J}_s = n_s e \mathbf{v}$$

Hence
$$\dot{\mathbf{J}}_s = \frac{n_s e^2}{m} \mathbf{E}$$

Taking the curl of both sides and using Maxwell equation (1), we get

$$\nabla \times \dot{\mathbf{J}}_s = \frac{n_s e^2}{m} \nabla \times \mathbf{E} = -\frac{n_s e^2}{mc} \dot{\mathbf{H}}$$

Integrating with respect to time, this yields

$$\nabla \times \left(\frac{mc}{n_s e^2} \right) \mathbf{J}_s = -\mathbf{H} + \beta(\text{const})$$

This is London's equation provided we arbitrarily set $\beta = 0$. We have no reason to do this; the reason, if it exists, is buried in the quantum mechanics of the problem and is, at this moment, invisible. However, ignoring this sticky fact, we now see that

$$\delta = \sqrt{\frac{\lambda c}{4\pi}} = \sqrt{\frac{mc^2}{4\pi n_s e^2}}$$

The above has, properly, the dimensions of a length.

All this has carried us a little further, since we now know everything except n_s, the number density of the superelectrons. However, we have a fairly good idea as to the number of conduction electrons per cubic centimeter in most metals from chemical considerations. We are also, intuitively, pretty sure n_s will be less than this number—probably a good deal less, near T_c. In any event, we have a sufficiency of knowledge to estimate the size of δ—whether it be nearer an angstrom or a meter. Taking mercury, for instance, we know that it possesses around two conduction electrons per atom. If we assume all these are superelectrons, then since we have the density and atomic weight, the above expression yields a value for $\delta \cong 1.7 \times 10^{-6}$ cm. Even if only 1 per cent of the conduction electrons are superelectrons, the estimate is still $\delta \approx 10^{-5}$ cm, which is certainly very tiny, as we had hoped.[1] To sum up, therefore, the London hypothesis has every appearance of being the correct formulation of the superconducting state. However, this is a matter for the experimentalists to decide by actual measurements of the London penetration depth.

THE EXPERIMENTAL SITUATION

The first physicist to attempt a measurement of δ was D. Shoenberg[2] in 1939 using the superconductor mercury, and his method involved measuring the magnetic susceptibility of small spheres in fields less than threshold. Since the susceptibility of superconductors is large, induction methods, such as those employed for paramagnetic salts, are usable. Now for a large (we will use the term "bulk") sphere, of radius much greater than δ, the susceptibility will be $-3/8\pi$, as Meissner found. If, however, the radius is comparable to δ, it will be less. This is due to the fact that, in this case, a substantial fraction of the sphere's volume will no longer have a zero magnetic induction

---

[1] For the semi-infinite geometry which we have used and with the external field H_0 uniform and parallel to the x direction, it is easy to show that

$$J_y = \frac{10H_0}{4\pi\delta} e^{-z/\delta} \qquad \text{amp/cm}^2$$

Thus, for a field $H_0 = 100$ gauss, which is less than critical for many superconductors, and assuming $\delta \approx 10^{-6}$ cm, we obtain a surface density for the supercurrent of the order of 10^8 amp/cm².

For the more realistic geometry, where we have a thin film of thickness $2a$ with H_0 parallel to its surface, we get

$$J_0 = \frac{10H_0}{4\pi\delta} \tanh \frac{a}{\delta}$$

For this case where a/δ is, say, $\frac{1}{10}$, $J_0 \sim 10^7$ amp/cm², which is still enormous.

[2] D. Shoenberg, *Nature*, **143**:434 (1939). A good account of his own and subsequent investigations will be found in his book, "Superconductivity," Cambridge University Press, New York, 1952.

due to the field penetration. Clearly, if B increases, the resulting diamagnetic susceptibility will decrease.[1]

The solution of Eq. (6) for the case of a sphere of radius a yields

$$\frac{\chi}{\chi_0} = 1 - \frac{3\delta}{a} \coth \frac{a}{\delta} + 3 \left(\frac{\delta}{a}\right)^2$$

which becomes

$$\frac{\chi}{\chi_0} \cong 1 - \frac{3\delta}{a} \qquad a \gg \delta \left(\frac{\chi}{\chi_0} \to 1 \qquad a \to \infty\right)$$

$$\frac{\chi}{\chi_0} \cong \frac{1}{15} \left(\frac{a}{\delta}\right)^2 \qquad a \ll \delta$$

A measurement of χ and a, for a sufficiently small sphere, will accordingly yield a value for δ, assuming, of course, that the London formulation is correct.

Shoenberg used mercury colloids distributed through a magnetically inert matrix (lard) to achieve the requisite sensitivity. Unfortunately, this pioneer measurement failed to come up with a value for δ. The reason for this lay in the fact that his colloids were not of uniform size and, more important, it proved unfeasible to measure their radii with any precision. Nevertheless, the measurement did reveal an important fact; namely, δ proved to be temperature dependent (see Fig. 81). As a matter of fact, this and later work have shown that the following expression is a good fit to the experiments, viz.,

$$\frac{\delta}{\delta_0} = \sqrt{\frac{1}{1 - (T/T_c)^4}}$$

Here δ_0 is the extrapolated penetration depth at $0°K$ and T_c is the superconducting transition temperature in zero field. These later measurements yield a value $\delta_0 = 4 \times 10^{-6}$ cm for mercury.

In the 20 years which have elapsed since the pioneer work, a very considerable amount of experimental effort has gone into field penetration studies. By and large it has confirmed the essential correctness

[1]
$$B = H + 4\pi(1 - n)I$$
$$\chi = \frac{I}{H} = \frac{1}{4\pi(1 - n)} \left(\frac{B - H}{H}\right)$$

where H is the *external* field and $n = \frac{1}{3}$ for a sphere. Thus for

$$B = 0 \qquad \chi_0 = -3/8\pi.$$

of the Londons' views.[1]   One of the best recent determinations of the
penetration depth is by Lock,[2] who measured the magnetic susceptibility of thin films evaporated onto mica plates using the elements Sn,
Pb, and In.   Here the thickness was accurately determinable by
weighing, and also good uniformity was assured.   In this case, of

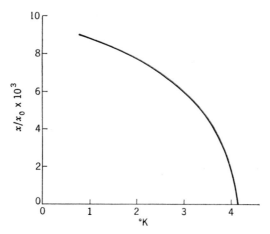

FIG. 81. The magnetic susceptibility of an aggregate of superconducting mercury colloids as a function of temperature.   According to the London theory
$\dfrac{\chi}{\chi_0} = \dfrac{1}{15}\left(\dfrac{a}{\delta}\right)^2$; hence this shows the variation of penetration depth with temperature.   (*Shoenberg*, 1940.)

course, we have to solve the London equation for thin flat plates rather
than spheres, and here

$$\frac{\chi}{\chi_0} = 1 - \frac{\delta}{a} \tanh \frac{a}{\delta}$$

or
$$\frac{\chi}{\chi_0} \cong 1 - \frac{\delta}{a} \qquad a > \delta$$

A plot of the resulting δ versus $(1 - t^4)^{-\frac{1}{2}}$ where $t \equiv T/T_c$ yielded a
straight line, which gives δ_0 by extrapolation.   These values for the

[1] It may have occurred to the reader to inquire as to whether or not there is a
penetration depth for the electric field E.   This has been looked for by observing
the capacity of a parallel-plate condenser made of superconducting metal as the
temperature was lowered through the transition.   If such an E penetration existed,
then the capacity should decrease, owing to field penetration, when it became
superconducting.   No such effect was found.

[2] J. M. Lock, *Proc. Roy. Soc.* (*London*), **A208**:391 (1951).

three elements are:

Element	δ_0
Sn	$(5.0 \pm 0.1) \times 10^{-6}$ cm
In	$(6.4 \pm 0.3) \times 10^{-6}$ cm
Pb	$(3.9 \pm 0.3) \times 10^{-6}$ cm

HIGH-FREQUENCY MEASUREMENTS

In 1940 H. London[1] reported some measurements on the resistance versus temperature curve for superconducting tin at a frequency of about 1,500 megacycles ($\lambda = 20.5$ cm). Figure 82 shows, very schematically, his experimental arrangement. The tin specimen ($T_c = 3.71°$K) was sealed in a small glass vessel which was connected to a manometer and volumetric gas-measuring device (flowmeter) outside the cryostat by a fine capillary. This vessel contained liquid helium. Surrounding this was an exchange-gas cavity similar to those used in specific-heat or paramagnetic-salt devices. The arrangement, therefore, constituted a vacuum calorimeter wherein any heat developed in the tin specimen could be measured by measuring the amount of helium evaporated from the glass vessel.

Surrounding the specimen vessel was a pair of brass "dees" formed by splitting a tube longitudinally. This pair was connected to a magnetron oscillator such that the whole was resonant at 20.5-cm wavelength.

In the normal state (i.e., above T_c) the high-frequency field induced currents in the tin which, in turn, produced Joule heat due to the specimen's resistance. As is well known, such currents are confined to a thin surface layer ("skin depth"). But, perhaps unexpectedly, Joule heat was also observed when the specimen became superconducting, and this was still finite at the lowest temperature reached in the experiment ($\sim 2°$K). This meant that, at this high frequency, the resistivity of the tin was no longer zero. Further, the ratio of heat evolved per second below and above T_c would, presumably, be equal to the ratio of the resistivities in the two phases. A plot of this ratio versus temperature is shown in Fig. 83.

In terms of the field penetration effect this result is not difficult to understand qualitatively. The fluctuating magnetic field inside the metal generates an alternating electric field in accordance with

$$\nabla \times \mathbf{E} = -\frac{1}{c}\frac{\partial \mathbf{H}}{\partial t}.$$ The higher the frequency, the higher this electric field proportionately, and it will generate a "normal" a-c current

[1] H. London, *Proc. Roy. Soc. (London)*, **A176**:522 (1940).

within the metal.   And such an electron flow will generate Joule heat as observed.   In the d-c case, on the other hand, no such electric field will be produced and, in consequence, no heat or resistivity.

Since London's first experiment, extensive microwave measurements have been made by several investigators.   In the modern work the

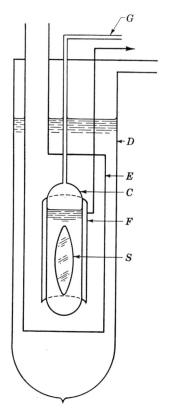

FIG. 82. Schematic of apparatus used to measure the resistivity of superconducting Sn at 1,500 megacycles.   D, helium Dewar; E, exchange gas can; S, tin specimen; C, glass capsule; F, high-frequency "dee"; G, Efflux gas line to measuring apparatus.   (H. London, 1940.)

specimens form resonance cavities, and the resistance is deduced from the shape of the resonance curves.   It is found that the higher the frequency, the greater the departure from zero resistance, as is made plausible above.   One interesting discovery, made by Pippard[1] as a result of this work, shows that the depth δ depends on the orientation of

[1] A. B. Pippard, *Proc. Roy. Soc. (London),* **A203** :98 (1950).

J_s with respect to the crystallographic axes in a tin monocrystal; i.e., the penetration depth is anisotropic.

SPECIFIC HEATS

As has been mentioned, the threshold curve represents a phase transition thermodynamically, and transitions across it, in view of the Meissner effect, look as if they ought to be reversible. Now such transitions are characterized by the fact that the Gibbs free energy $F = u + pv - TS$ is conserved.[1] Clearly, for a reversible transformation,

$$dF = du + p\,dv - T\,dS + v\,dp - s\,dT$$
$$= v\,dp - S\,dT$$

or
$$\frac{\partial F}{\partial T} = -S$$

Suppose we return to our superconducting wire and place it in a uniform magnetic field parallel to the axis and thence cool it down through the transition. When the temperature reaches the threshold-curve boundary, the field inside the volume V of the wire is ejected. This is caused by the appearance of a complex distribution of supercurrents whose field just annuls the applied field. But these currents possess kinetic energy, derived from the field, whose value must be $H_c^2 V/8\pi$, the energy resident in their field. Hence if we call the thermal free energies of the two phases F_n and F_s, respectively, then the total free energy of the normal phase will be F_n while the other, due to the current, will be $F_s + H_c^2 V/8\pi$. If the transition is reversible, these two must be equal, i.e.,

$$F_n = F_s + \frac{H_c^2 V}{8\pi}$$

i.e., differentiating,

$$-S_n = -S_s + \frac{V}{4\pi} H_c \frac{dH_c}{dT}$$

But dH_c/dT is clearly always negative, and hence

$$S_s < S_n$$

This means that, for whatever reason, the superconducting state is a more ordered state than the normal one.

Again, since $dS = (C/T)\,dT$, where C is the specific heat, by a second differentiation with respect to T we have

$$C_s - C_n = \frac{VT}{4\pi} \left[H_c \frac{d^2 H_c}{dT^2} + \left(\frac{dH_c}{dT} \right)^2 \right]$$

[1] For instance, the condensation of a vapor into a liquid phase.

Thus if we cool the specimen in zero external field ($H_c = 0$) through the transition, there will be a "jump" in the specific heat of an amount

$$\frac{VT_c}{4\pi}\left(\frac{dH_c}{dT}\right)^2_{T=T_c}$$

Figure 84 shows the result of such an experiment, for the superconductor tantalum, which is in good agreement with the above. All

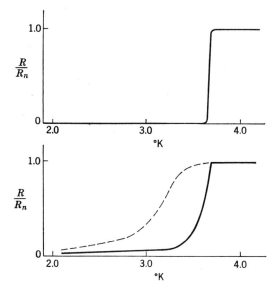

FIG. 83. The normalized resistance of Sn as a function of temperature. *Upper curve*—d-c measurement (student exercise); *lower curve*—solid line, 1,500 megacycles (*H. London*, 1940); dotted line, 1.7×10^5 megacycles. (*Forrester et al.*, 1958.)

this, of course, proves no more than that the superconductive transition is a reversible one.

The fact that the entropies in the two states differ suggests a possibility for low-temperature cooling which was first tried out by Mendelssohn. In Fig. 85 the entropy versus temperature for the two states is sketched. Imagine a superconducting specimen at temperature T_i ($\sim1°$K) in an adiabatic container, similar to the type used for magnetic cooling or specific-heat work, all in zero magnetic field, so that the specimen is superconducting (point A). Assume now that a field is switched on of sufficient magnitude to restore the metal to its normal state. Since the process is adiabatic and reversible, the entropy may not change; hence the specimen must cool to a lower temperature (point B) T_f.   This is rather the reverse of the process used with the paramagnetic salt.

Using a "hard" superconductor, i.e., one with a high threshold field, quite substantial drops in temperature occur.   Unfortunately, however, the method is of only marginal practical value because of the very small specific heat of the metals at the low temperatures (cf. the paramagnetic salt discussed in Chap. 1).

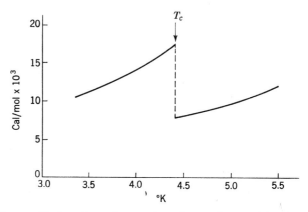

FIG. 84. The specific-heat jump in tantalum due to the transition into superconductivity in zero magnetic field.   (*Desirant and Mendelsohn.*)

One interesting result of the field penetration emerges from the above.   It was long ago observed, experimentally, that the magnetic threshold for a specimen of small dimensions is *larger* than the threshold for the same material in bulk (see Fig. 86).   In the small specimen (i.e., at least one dimension $\sim\delta$) the magnetic term in the free energy is reduced since, because of penetration, a comparatively large fraction of its volume still contains flux below T_c.   If we make the reasonable assumption that the thermal plus magnetic free energies (per unit mass) are independent of specimen size, then

$$F_s + \frac{H_c{}^2}{8\pi} = F_s + \frac{\alpha H_c^{*2}}{8\pi} \qquad 0 < \alpha < 1$$

where H_c, H_c^* are, respectively, the threshold fields of the bulk and small specimens and α is a number less than unity, i.e.,

$$H_c^* = \frac{H_c}{\sqrt{\alpha}}$$

or $$H_c^* > H_c$$

The specific heat of nonsuperconducting metals shows a temperature variation, at low temperatures, composed of two terms—the usual Debye T^3 term plus one, linear in T, which arises from the small specific heat of the conduction electrons as a consequence of Fermi statistics. For many years it was believed that superconductors showed only a Debye term, with the electronic term absent. Recent measurements, however, by Corak et al.[1] have shown this to be incor-

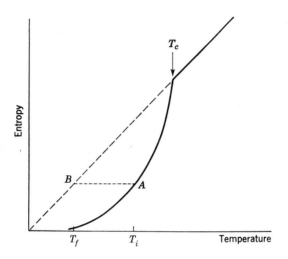

FIG. 85. Technique of cooling by use of a superconductor, due to Mendelssohn.

rect. In the case of superconducting vanadium ($T_c \cong 5°\text{K}$) these authors found that, below about $0.7T_c$, the electronic contribution to the specific heat followed the law

$$\frac{C_{\text{el}}}{\gamma T_c} = ae^{-bT_c/T}$$

Here a, b, and γ are numerical constants. In addition, although the experimental data are somewhat meager, such a temperature dependence is probably true for superconductors in general.

This is revealing, since such an exponential term is characteristic of an energy gap in the electronic spectrum. We recall an analogous case in the roton excitation spectrum in Landau's theory of He II where the gap was introduced for the purpose of achieving a fast exponential decay of the roton density (and specific heat) below 1°K.

[1] Corak, Goodman, Satterthwaite, and Wexler, *Phys. Rev.*, **102**:656 (1956).

THE ISOTOPE EFFECT

In the long history of superconductivity many experiments have been tried in the hope of finding an "effect." Sometimes these were predicated on very naïve ideas, often on no theoretical picture at all—they were what we might call "shot in the dark" experiments. But all this is very legitimate; it happens that such procedures have yielded considerable dividends in the past and very likely will continue to do so in the future. The isotope effect is a prime example of the utility of this kind of experimentation.

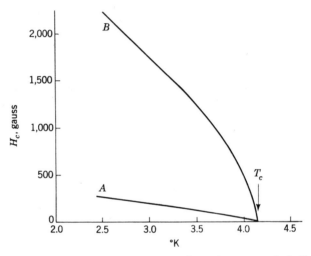

FIG. 86. Threshold field curves for mercury. *Curve A,* mercury in bulk; *curve B,* mercury film 596 A thick. (*Appleyard et al.,* 1939.)

This effect, discovered simultaneously and independently in 1950 by Reynolds, Serin, Wright, and Nesbitt[1] and by Maxwell,[2] is that in superconducting mercury, the transition temperature depends on the average isotopic mass of the sample. Since that time the effect has been confirmed by several investigators and found in several other elements. Reynolds and Serin were the first to point out that the relationship between the transition temperature T_c and the average atomic weight of the samples, M, was given by a simple relationship, namely,

$$T_c M^{1/2} = \text{const}$$

[1] C. A. Reynolds, B. Serin, W. H. Wright, and L. B. Nesbitt, *Phys. Rev.,* **78**:487 (1950).

[2] E. Maxwell, *Phys. Rev.,* **78**:477 (1950).

Referring back to Chap. 5, where we discussed the linear lattice of particles, it will be recalled that the allowed frequencies are inversely proportional to the square root of the particle mass. Further, in Debye's theory of specific heats, the Debye temperature θ is proportional to the maximum allowed frequency, i.e., $h\nu_{max} = k\theta$.

It follows therefore that

$$\theta \sim \frac{1}{M^{1/2}}$$

and so $T_c \sim \theta$. The isotope experiments suggest, therefore, that the appearance of superconductivity is, in some way, bound up with an

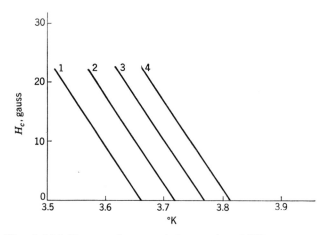

FIG. 87. Threshold field curves for several tin samples of different average atomic weight. The average weights are as follows: 1, 123.01; 2, 119.78; 3, 116.67; 4, 113.58. (*E. Maxwell*, 1952.)

electron-lattice interaction—a very far-reaching idea, as will emerge.

Figure 87, taken from a paper by Maxwell,[1] shows some threshold fields for tin isotopes in small fields wherein the plots are seen to be accurately parallel—a feature which persists to lowest temperatures and highest fields. As a result, it follows that the threshold field at absolute zero (H_0) likewise varies as $M^{-1/2}$.

MISCELLANEOUS PROPERTIES

We have now discussed the main empirical properties of the superconducting state, and in this section we consider some others. Thus the Hall effect in a superconductor below the threshold curve is

[1] E. Maxwell, *Phys. Rev.*, **86**:235 (1952).

zero. This means that the supercurrents are not affected by a magnetic field which is less than critical. The Seebeck emf (thermoelectric effect) is zero at a junction of two superconductors both of which are in the superconducting phase. On the other hand, there is such an emf between two wires of the same metal when one of them has the superconductivity removed by applying to it a field beyond critical.

One intriguing, though not especially fundamental, effect is concerned with what is generally called the "intermediate" state. To illustrate, suppose a superconducting sphere is placed in an initially uniform magnetic field pointing along a diameter. When the sphere goes superconducting, the flux is ejected and the field in the vicinity of the sphere is no longer uniform. At the equator the field is in the same direction as before but has a magnitude of $\frac{3}{2}H_0$.[1] But when H_0 becomes $\frac{2}{3}H_c$, this means that the field at the equator just becomes critical, which destroys the superconductivity there but leaves it intact elsewhere, since $\frac{3}{2}H_0$ is the highest value of the field anywhere on the sphere's surface. However, the condition that the field at the equator shall be $\frac{3}{2}H_0$ is predicated on the whole sphere being superconducting (i.e., $\mu = 0$). Hence the situation is, energetically speaking, unstable.

It turns out that the energy is minimal when the sphere "splits" into regions alternately superconducting and nonsuperconducting. These normal regions are slices bounded by planes parallel to H_0. Thus if we measure the d-c resistance (1) along a diameter in the H_0 direction and then (2) at right angles to this, we get a finite resistance in the second case and zero in the first! Actually powder patterns (similar to the Bitter patterns showing ferromagnetic domains) can be formed on a hemisphere. The powder, which in this case is made of some high-threshold superconductor, heaps up in the superconductive regions since it is ejected from the normal regions where lines of force enter the sphere. This is due, of course, to the high diamagnetism of the powder.

All the presently known superconducting elements in the periodic table are given in Appendix 1. The metal bismuth, as occurring in nature, is not one of them, at least down to ($\sim 0.05°K$). However, it

---

[1] For a sphere of permeability μ this is, from the solution of Laplace's equation for the potential,

$$\frac{3H_0}{\mu + 2}$$

The Meissner effect is equivalent to $\mu = 0$.

has been found possible to "persuade" bismuth to become a super-conductor. This has been accomplished by depositing the metal, from its vapor, onto a surface cooled to liquid-helium temperature. The film so produced is found to become superconducting at about 6°K. This is undoubtedly due to a crystal modification caused by the production process; the electron diffraction pattern is different from that in ordinary bismuth. By "annealing" the film at 20°K, the bismuth structure is regained and the superconductivity disappears.

THE QUESTION OF AN ENERGY GAP IN THE ELECTRONIC SPECTRUM

The discovery of an exponential specific heat for supercon-ductors, as already discussed, is an indication of the existence of an energy gap in the spectrum of those electrons responsible for super-conductivity. In the last 5 years or so experimental evidence strongly supporting this view has been steadily accumulating. At this point, therefore, it will be useful to try to form some mental picture of the electronic spectrum. This picture, which is based largely on the BCS[1] theory of superconductivity, is as follows.

At $T > T_c$ all the electrons are "normal," i.e., ordinary conduction electrons. As we reduce the temperature, a number of these become "superfluid"; i.e., they "condense" into a ground state of zero entropy, and between these condensed and normal electrons there exists an energy gap. This energy gap is zero at T_c but increases in value as we go down in temperature, finally reaching a value of a few times kT_c at absolute zero. This is a very different situation from, say the roton spectrum in liquid helium wherein, as we know, the energy gap is temperature independent and of fixed value. In the ground state the electron flow is quite frictionless, but if, in some way, we excite an electron over this gap, it loses its frictionless properties and becomes normal. An obvious, but not usefully controllable, way of supplying enough energy to bridge the gap is to supply some heat. A better way is to allow a photon to do the job. By order of magnitude we should require $h\nu = kT_c$ which for aluminum ($T_c \sim 1°K$), for instance, would require $\nu \cong 20,000$ megacycles, a microwave frequency.

Figure 88 shows a result, due to Biondi and Garfunkel,[2] in which the normalized resistance of aluminum is plotted against the reduced tem-perature $t = T/T_c$. These measurements extend down to close to 0.3°K by the use of an He[3] refrigerator. For photon energies less than

[1] BCS = Bardeen, Cooper, Schrieffer—the principal architects of the theory.
[2] M. A. Biondi and M. P. Garfunkel, *Phys. Rev.*, **116**:853 (1959).

about $3kT_c$ the curves extrapolate accurately to zero at 0°K, whereas
for greater energies than this they do not. This means that at the
absolute zero, superelectrons are not excited over the gap for energies
less than about $3kT_c$; i.e., this is the value of the gap at 0°K. At tem-

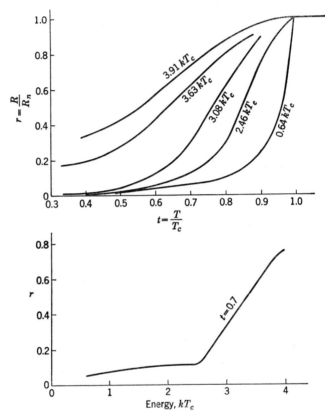

FIG. 88. Microwave measurements in aluminum to determine the BCS energy gap.
(*Biondi and Garfunkel*, 1959.)

peratures between $t = 0$ and $t = 1$ the gap value is determinable as
follows.

We construct an isotherm at some fixed t by plotting $r \equiv R/R_n$ as a
function of the photon energy. Figure 88 shows a typical plot for
$t = 0.7$. As we see, r stays substantially constant until the energy
reaches $\sim 2.6kT_c$, whence it increases rapidly. We interpret this to
mean that the dissipation r, below $2.6kT_c$, is due to electrons which
have been thermally excited through the gap. The rapid rise in r

beyond $2.6kT_c$ arises from added superelectrons which have become normal by being excited through the gap by this photon energy; i.e., $2.6kT_c$ is the gap at $t = 0.7$.

Figure 89 shows the resulting gap as a function of temperature compared with the BCS prediction. It thus appears that the model is fairly analogous to the Landau roton model for He II, except for the temperature dependence of the gap. And the reason for superfluidity is the same in both cases; namely, the electron stream in the condensed phase will be frictionless until it acquires sufficient velocity to lose energy by exciting an electron through the gap. There is therefore a

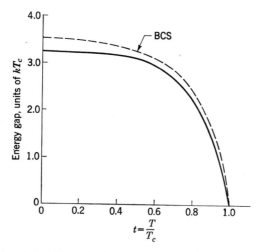

FIG. 89. Experimentally determined energy gap between super and normal electrons in aluminum. (*Biondi and Garfunkel*, 1959.)

critical velocity, temperature dependent, of which the critical threshold field is a measure. It is no accident, therefore, that Fig. 89 has the same general appearance as the threshold curve.

While the above experiment seems fairly convincing, it must be admitted that energy-gap measurements on other superconductors are greatly to be desired. In this connection Tinkham, using far infrared absorption in thin films of several superconductors, has found that the gap at absolute zero (ε_0) varies from $4.7kT_c$ for mercury to $2.8kT_c$ for niobium. This compares to the universal value of $3.52kT_c$ in the BCS theory.[1] Further, he finds that a plot of ε_0 versus Debye temperature falls on a smooth curve on which the above result for Al also lies.

[1] Unpublished results quoted by Biondi and Garfunkel, *ibid.*

THE NATURE OF THE BCS MODEL

In framing a theory of superconductivity we are confronted, at the outset, with what appears to be something of a dilemma, namely, the statistics of the particles (Fermi for electrons.)[1] We have seen that, in the case of He^3, this same statistic precludes superfluidity. However, a metal and a liquid differ in that the latter does not possess an ionic lattice. It is this difference, as we shall see, which removes the dilemma.

It will be useful, at this point, to recall what we know concerning an ordinary or normal (i.e., nonsuperconducting) metal, which is the so-called Sommerfeld-Bloch theory. The wave functions are of the single-particle type, and, because of the exclusion principle, not more than two electrons (with opposite spins) may possess the same wave function, i.e., be in the same state. However, the energies of different states may be the same (degeneracy).

At $0°K$ all the lowest states are occupied up to a point determined by the total number of electrons available. This means that the electron energies vary from zero (nearly) up to some value E_F, which may be quite large—the order of several electron volts. If we make a plot of the energy versus the wave vector, or momentum, we get a sphere whose surface E_F is called the Fermi surface. Actually what we have so far described is the "free electron" case wherein, as a first approximation, the potential energy due to the lattice ions and electron cloud is taken as constant.

The next better approximation (Bloch) is one in which this potential is taken as spatially periodic. In this case, certain geometric surfaces in the k space form planes of discontinuous energy (Brillouin zones). In any one of these zones there is just one state per atom; i.e., for a monovalent element (e.g., Na) a zone is just half filled. In this case the electron population is such that the Fermi surface is far from such boundaries, and it is still nearly spherical.

Now the states above the Fermi surface are, at $0°K$, unoccupied. But if we feed a little heat into the system, some electrons below E_F are excited into these vacant states, leaving vacant places (holes) below E_F. In some lattices (e.g., carbon in the diamond structure) there is an

---

[1] That the supercurrents are really electron currents and not, for instance, in some way connected with the electron spin was first demonstrated some 20 years ago by Kikoin and Goobar. These authors measured the angular momentum acquired by the specimen when the supercurrent was created by a magnetic field. The result yields a Landé g factor of unity, which means that the diamagnetism is due to ordinary electron currents.

energy gap between E_F and the unoccupied states.   If we apply an
electric field to our model, all the electrons below E_F will acquire
momentum and hence kinetic energy, *but only if there are vacant states
available to them.*   Generally there are, but in the case of diamond there
are none unless the field is so intense as to bridge the gap.   Hence in
this case there is no induced motion and no current, and the substance
is an insulator.   It still contains plenty of "free" electrons, but they
have no place to go.   On the other hand, for carbon atoms in a different lattice (graphite) there is no gap, and the substance is a fair conductor of electricity.   This illustrates a point which, on classical
theory, would be quite incomprehensible.

The Bloch waves, in an ideal lattice at 0°K, move without hindrance
through the lattice until a zone boundary is reached, whence they are
reflected.   But these waves are easily scattered by imperfections in
the lattice, such as impurity atoms or dislocations, and by phonons.
Such scattering results in energy dissipation or ohmic resistance, so on
this model we would get nothing like superconductivity, which is a
frictionless flow in quite impure metals at finite temperatures.   It has
been long apparent, therefore, that a theory of superconductivity must
involve a higher order of approximation than that of Bloch's model.
Said differently, we must consider more interaction than the simple
periodic potential of the Bloch model.   The stumbling block here lies
in the fact that there are a great number of possibilities, and the isotope
effect was really the clue which sorted them out.

The success of the BCS model[1] rests, fundamentally, on choosing
the correct (out of many) interaction term between electrons in con-
structing the Hamiltonian of the system.   It turns out that there is a
strong attraction between *pairs* of electrons which arises as a result of
the following mechanism.   At 0°K an electron moving through the
lattice (there are no "thermal" phonons) distorts or polarizes it.   In
the language of field theory we would say that it creates a "virtual"
phonon.   A second electron will "feel" this lattice polarization and so
be coupled to the first.   It turns out that such correlated pairs are of
opposite spin and zero total momentum in their ground state.   The
wave functions of such correlated states prove to be very rigid; i.e.,
unlike those in Bloch states, they are not much scattered by such
things as thermal phonons or impurities.   Further, it takes a small but
finite amount of energy to break up these pairs and scatter the electrons into Bloch states.   This amounts to introducing an energy gap

[1] Bardeen, Cooper, and Schrieffer, *Phys. Rev.*, **108**:1175 (1957).   A less formal
version is given by Cooper in *Am. J. Phys.*, **28**:91 (1960), from which much of our
account is taken.

into the electronic spectrum.   Thus, in a sense, the superfluidity (i.e., rigidity) of these wave functions is a consequence of this energy gap (cf. the similar situation with respect to the rotons in He II).

In an infinitely rigid lattice or one composed of infinitely massive ions no such correlation could occur.[1]   Also we should not expect it to be important in those metals which exhibit a weak electron-phonon interaction in normal circumstances.   Since the ohmic resistance results from this, we should not expect good electrical conductors (e.g., Cu, Ag) to become superconductors—a fact borne out in practice.

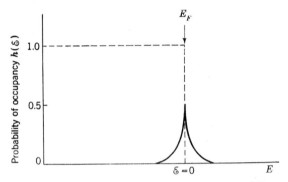

FIG. 90. The probability of occupancy of the pair states at 0°K as a function of the energy E where $\epsilon = E - E_F$ is measured from the Fermi surface E_F.   The dotted graph represents the Sommerfeld-Bloch model of a normal metal in which all the states are occupied below E_F and none above.   The horizontal scale is greatly exaggerated since, for the pair states, $h(\epsilon) \sim 0$ when the energy of a pair $\epsilon \sim 10^{-3}$ ev.   By comparison, E_F is ~ 5 ev.   Hence the pair states cluster around the Fermi surface.

It turns out that these pair-correlated states are confined, in momentum space, to a narrow shell in the vicinity of the Fermi surface (Fig. 90), and the wave functions of the superelectrons extend over large distances in ordinary space—of the order of 10^{-4} cm, which is large on an atomic scale.[2]

[1] This is consistent with the isotope effect, since $M \to \infty$ $T_c \to 0$, i.e., no superconductivity in this case.

[2] The idea that wave functions are spread out arose earlier than the BCS work and was the result of Pippard's work. Using microwave techniques, he measured the penetration depth in tin as a function of the magnetic field just up to critical. It turned out that δ was substantially the same at $H \approx 0$ and $H \approx H_c$ (Fig. 91). This means that the entropy density due to the field, in the thin layer δ, would be prohibitive. To get around this, Pippard proposed that the entropy change occurs in a much thicker layer which he evaluated as about 10^{-4} cm. This distance, in the literature, is known as the "coherence distance" and is a measure of long-range order in the sense that density of superelectrons (and associ-

As stated, the preferred (i.e., minimal energy configuration) ground state for the pairs is one of opposite spin and zero total momentum, and clearly this would not produce a persistent current. It happens, however, that rigid wave functions can exist, for opposite spin pairs, which have the same momentum, albeit the energy of these is higher than the ground state.

Actually, as Bardeen has pointed out,[1] there is a fairly close analogy between superconductivity and Landau's model for superfluid helium, although, of course, the physical mechanisms in the two cases are

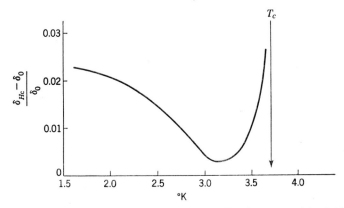

FIG. 91. The very slight difference in penetration depth measured in fields near critical (δ_{H_c}) compared with that measured in fields near zero (δ_0) for Sn. (*Pippard*, 1950.)

quite different.   One can, in BCS, formally divide the electron fluid into ρ_s and ρ_n components.   The former are due to the pair states, and the latter are the ordinary Bloch-Sommerfeld states.   As in Landau's theory, where there is an energy gap between the roton ground state and the superfluid, so also is there a gap between the pair states and the Bloch states.   This gap is, however, temperature dependent, vanishing at T_c, whereas Landau's Δ is a constant.

The excitation spectrum for the normal-component electrons in BCS is

$$E(p) = \left[\left(\frac{p^2}{2m} - E_F \right)^2 + \varepsilon_0{}^2 \right]^{1/2}$$

ated wave functions) must vary only slowly within this distance. In light of all this, the London equation needs modification—the relation between J_s and H can no longer be a point relation involving differentials but must rather be an integral relation involving the field about the point in question, extending over the coherence distance.

[1] J. Bardeen, *Phys. Rev. Letters*, **1**:399 (1958).

which is reminiscent of, though of course different from, the roton spectrum in He II.   Here E_F is the energy of the Fermi surface and ε_0 the BCS energy gap.

The same arguments which Landau used to compute the superfluid critical velocity apply equally well here.   These arguments show, it will be recalled, that

$$v_c = \left\langle \frac{E(p)}{p} \right\rangle_{min}$$

For the above spectrum, remembering that $\varepsilon_0 \ll E_F$, this yields

$$v_c \cong \frac{\varepsilon_0}{\sqrt{2mE_F}}$$

Thus the critical velocity needed to destroy the superfluidity vanishes when ε_0 vanishes; i.e., the superfluidity is a direct consequence of the energy gap between condensed and excited states.

Typically, at $0°K$, $\varepsilon_0 \sim 10^{-3}$ ev and $E_F \sim 5$ ev, whence the above expression yields $v_c \sim 100$ m/sec.   Hence a stream of superfluid electrons (n_s per unit volume) would give rise to a supercurrent density which may not exceed $n_s e v_c$.   The resulting field due to this current must therefore be the critical threshold field of the superconductor, which vanishes when $\varepsilon_0 = 0$, i.e., at $T = T_c$.   In the case of mercury, assuming all the conduction electrons are in paired states at $0°K$, $n_s \sim 4 \times 10^{22}$ and so $J_s \sim 6 \times 10^7$ amp/cm², which, as we saw previously, is a reasonable figure.   Bardeen shows, for small velocities, that

$$\rho_n = \frac{4\pi}{3h^3} \int_0^\infty p^4 \frac{d}{dE} \left(\frac{1}{e^{E(p)/kT} + 1} \right) dp$$

which is identical with Landau's result (Chap. 5) except that Fermi instead of Bose statistics are used.

In some respects the BCS theory is superior to Landau's theory of He II since, in the former, the frictionless character of the superfluid emerges directly because of the nature of the wave functions of the paired states.   But in the latter the theory is almost all concerned with the excited phase—the frictionless character of the superfluid comes out only indirectly as a result of the "critical velocity" calculation.

The above expression for ρ_n shows that there will be some Bloch-state particles at any finite temperature and these, below T_c, will coexist with the paired particles.   We appear, therefore, to have the basic ingredients for a second sound in the superconductor.   Such an effect has not been observed, and this is probably due to the very large "viscosity" of the normal fluid, i.e., the high attenuation of the normal component flow caused by interaction with the ionic lattice. Second sound in He II has not been observed in very narrow channels or in the Rollin film for an analogous reason; viz., in these cases the normal fluid cannot move because of the effect of its viscosity.

The Bloch electrons, in a normal metal, show a weak paramagnetism at 0°K. This comes about from the electron spin moment, which is large, but because of the exclusion principle, only a few more electrons are parallel to the field than are opposed, which makes the whole effect weak but measurable. Since the correlated pairs are of opposite spin, this means that the spin susceptibility in a superconductor at 0°K should vanish. This point, as will emerge, has been investigated experimentally and is one of the few predictions of BCS not in accord with the experiments.

The stickiest point in the whole BCS theory is the question as to whether or not it legitimately shows a Meissner effect or, said differently, can properly prove London's postulated field equation connecting J_s and H. For some time this key point has been a matter for dispute among theoreticians. It appears, however, that the model does properly show a flux expulsion.[1]

Thus it appears that the BCS model is most probably a correct description of the phenomenon of superconductivity in first approximation. It is, in fact, a remarkably versatile theory, being in concordance with the great majority of "fundamental" effects which are observed. It will not, of course, pinpoint a certain element and predict that it will or will not be a superconductor. However, even in this direction it goes some distance, since it shows that metals with weak electron-phonon interaction (i.e., good electrical conductors) are not likely to become superconducting. Further, the magnitude of the pair correlation energies is such that it assures us that superconductivity is a "low-temperature" phenomenon. Those optimists who are hopeful of discovering a room-temperature superconductor, a most useful gadget, seem doomed to failure. Having said this much, we shall now turn to some few experiments in which a lack of concordance with the BCS model is found.

THE KNIGHT SHIFT

In this phenomenon we find that, in a given field H, the frequency ν_m at which nuclear resonance is observed in a metal is higher than the frequency ν_i at which it occurs, for the same nucleus, in an

[1] P. W. Anderson, *Phys. Rev.*, **112**:1900 (1958).

insulator.   The ratio $K \equiv (\nu_m - \nu_i)/\nu_i$ is called the Knight shift after its discoverer, and the effect is due to the presence of conduction electrons in the metal.

It turns out that the difference $(\nu_m - \nu_i)$ is due to the presence of a local magnetic field, at the nucleus, produced by the conduction electrons.   Thus if $\psi(0)$ is the wave function, at the nucleus, of a conduction electron near the Fermi surface and χ is the paramagnetic spin susceptibility of the conduction electrons, then

$$K = \frac{\nu_m - \nu_i}{\nu_i} \sim \langle |\psi(0)|^2 \rangle_{\text{av}} \chi$$

The Knight shift is therefore a measure of the Pauli spin paramagnetism in a metal[1] and so also a measure of the density of states at the Fermi surface.   This is just the sort of tool we need to explore the BCS theory, since the correlated states are near the Fermi surface and, further, such pairs have no net magnetic moment.   Also, since the energy involved in the superconducting transition is small, it is unlikely that the value $\psi(0)$ of the wave function of a conducting electron at the position of a nucleus is appreciably affected when the specimen goes superconducting.   It would thus appear to be of great interest to investigate the Knight shift in a superconductor from above T_c to as close to $0°K$ as is reachable, because at this last temperature, owing to the pair correlation, the Knight shift should vanish.

Since magnetic resonance experiments involve microwave frequencies and we have to get these fields into the bulk of the specimen,

---

[1] At $0°K$ the conduction electrons occupy a set of states extending from zero energy to the value at the Fermi surface.   Because of the exclusion principle only two electrons, with spins opposite, have the same wave function.   Above there is a similar quasi-continuum of vacant states.   When a magnetic field H is applied, the energies of those with parallel (to the field) spins tend to be lowered by $-\mu H$, where μ is the spin moment of the electron.   Since all lower levels below the Fermi surface are occupied, the parallels have nowhere to go, but the entire antiparallel population is shifted up in energy (by μH), since higher states are unoccupied. This, however, is an unstable situation—some antiparallels "umklapp" into now available lower (parallel) energy states above E_F, and the rest drop back into the lowest available antiparallel states.   The net result is that we end up with more electrons parallel than antiparallel; this excess occupies a set of states (with now one electron per state) over a range of energy of $2\mu H$.   Since $E_F \sim$ several electron volts and $2\mu H \sim 10^{-4}$ ev for 10,000 gauss, these singly occupied states are very close to the Fermi surface.   Since also the density of states per unit energy range (ρ_F) at E_F is $\gamma E_F^{1/2}$, where $\gamma = \frac{V}{4\pi^2} \left(\frac{2m}{\hbar^2} \right)^{3/2}$, the excess of parallel electrons is $2\mu H \gamma E_F^{1/2}$ and hence the magnetic moment of the gas, in the direction of H, will be $2\mu^2 H \gamma E_F^{1/2}$.   Hence the paramagnetic susceptibility is $2\mu^2 \gamma E_F^{1/2}$, i.e., $K \sim \langle |\psi(0)|^2 \rangle_{\text{av}} \rho_F$.

this suggests we use colloids or thin films of comparable size to the penetration depth. A very good example of this kind of measurement has been carried out by Reif,[1] from whose paper most of the preceding remarks have been taken. The superconductor chosen for the test was mercury, for a number of reasons. Colloidal particles, produced by reducing $HgNO_3$ with hydrazone, were confined to a matrix consisting of egg albumen hydrolyzed with NaOH. The samples contained around 70 per cent Hg by weight. Electron-microscope observations showed the colloids to be spherical with diameters cluster-

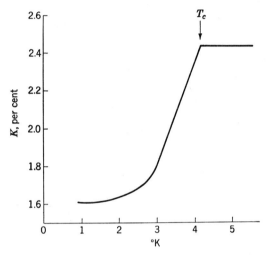

FIG. 92. The Knight shift as a function of temperature for superconducting mercury colloids in a field of 967 gauss. (*Reif*, 1957.)

ing around the penetration depth δ_0. The fact that the small specimens have a much higher threshold field than that of bulk mercury is, of course, a considerable advantage in this type of work where high fields are desirable from the electronics viewpoint.

This experiment, like most in modern work on superconductivity, is far from simple in both execution and interpretation. Nevertheless, the result (Fig. 92) seems quite definite. Pretty surely K is not approaching a zero value at $0°K$, and we seem to have a disagreement with the BCS prediction[2] of a rather fundamental kind.

Androes and Knight[3] have performed a Knight-shift experiment on

[1] F. Reif, *Phys. Rev.*, **106**:208 (1957).

[2] The calculation, due to Yosida [*Phys. Rev.*, **110**:769 (1958)] and based on BCS, predicts an exponentially vanishing susceptibility at $0°K$.

[3] G. M. Androes and W. D. Knight, *Phys. Rev. Letters*, **2**:386 (1959).

superconducting Sn using evaporated films instead of colloids. These have the advantage, as was the case with penetration-depth measurements, of being more uniform than colloids in their dimensions. The result, again, is that the nuclear magnetic resonance shift does not go to zero as $T \rightarrow 0°K$.

A considerable number of suggestions have been made by various investigators in an effort to "fix up" the BCS model on this point, and it seems safe to predict that these experiments will not prove fatal to BCS. Rather, the situation is likely a result of the fact, previously mentioned, that the BCS theory is really a first approximation which, undoubtedly, will be subject to further refinements.

ELECTRONIC SPECIFIC HEATS

The fact that the BCS model is a first approximation shows up in other directions where sufficient experimental evidence has been accumulated. Boorse[1] has made a careful study of all the available data on the electronic specific heat in superconductors (Al, Zn, V) and compared it with the BCS prediction. He finds that for $t = T/T_c$ lying in the range from 0.5 to 0.25 the experiments and the theory are in good accord. However, for t less than about 0.25 the agreement becomes increasingly worse; i.e., at $t < 0.25$ there is a definite departure from the exponential behavior for various superconductors, although the extent of this departure varies with the element in question.

Cooper[2] has suggested that the above departures might very well be accounted for by a variation in the magnitude of the energy gap over the Fermi surface and presents some rough calculations which seem to support this idea.

ATTENUATION OF ULTRASONICS

In 1955 Mackinnon and also Mason and Bömmel observed that the attenuation of an ultrasonic compressional wave in a pure superconductor decreased sharply as the temperature was reduced below T_c. On the other hand, in the normal state of the superconductor the attenuation was substantially temperature independent. This effect has been studied with considerable finesse and in much detail by Morse and Bohm,[3] among others. Figure 93 shows a fairly typical result for a single crystal of Sn at 33.5 megacycles.

[1] H. A. Boorse, *Phys. Rev. Letters*, **2**:391 (1959).

[2] L. N. Cooper, *Phys. Rev. Letters*, **3**:17 (1959).

[3] R. W. Morse and H. B. Bohm, *Phys. Rev.*, **108**:1094 (1957).

In this work the pulsed ultrasonics are generated by a quartz piezo-electric crystal, driven from a suitable oscillator and sealed to one of two accurately parallel faces of the metallic crystal. The quartz crystal, which is used as both a transmitter and a receiver, measures the attenuation by comparing pulse heights of the transmitted pulse and reflected echo from the other crystal face. A suitable external field permits investigation of the superconductor in its normal state at any temperature. The velocity of sound in the metal can also, of course, be determined from a time-of-flight measurement on the echoes. This does not change at the transition.

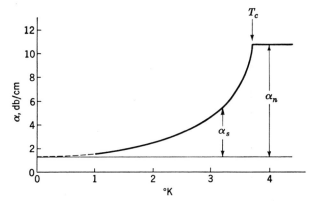

FIG. 93. The attenuation suffered by pulses of 33.5-megacycle sound in a tin single crystal. The finite attenuation at 0°K is due to lattice dissipation; the differences α_s and α_n are due to electrons. (*Morse and Bohm*, 1957.)

As Fig. 93 shows, the attenuation extrapolates to a reasonably constant value at the absolute zero, which is very much less than its constant value above T_c. This suggests, perhaps a little naïvely, that the large drop in attenuation in the superconducting region is due to the increasing growth of the population of superelectrons which, since they do not react with the lattice, are incapable of absorbing the ultrasonic energy. The constant value of the attenuation at 0°K is therefore that due to irreversible effects in the lattice itself. By subtracting it, we therefore get the true electronic contribution α_s or α_n.

On the BCS model, however, the absorption mechanism would be different. Here the pairs have to receive sufficient energy from the ultrasonic wave to excite them over the energy gap. Since the latter increases as the reduced temperature t decreases, clearly, by this mechanism, the attenuation will decrease as t is lowered. In fact, the calculation (by Bardeen) shows that

$$\frac{\alpha_s}{\alpha_n} = \frac{2}{e^{1.75/t} + 1}$$

Figure 94 shows a plot of α_s/α_n versus t for experiments with tin and indium, compared to the BCS value given by the above expression.

It is seen that the agreement here is extremely good and constitutes another proof of the existence of the BCS energy gap. It will be recalled that a possible explanation for the specific-heat discrepancy for small values of t, as discussed by Boorse, might lie in an energy gap which is different for different crystal orientations.

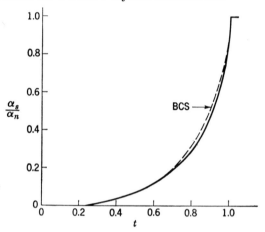

FIG. 94. The ratio of the two attenuations as a function of the reduced temperature for tin and indium, compared with the BCS prediction. (*Morse and Bohm*, 1957.)

Morse, Olsen, and Gavenda[1] have investigated this possibility by the ultrasound attenuation technique. Single crystals of tin were used, and the specimens were chosen such that the sound was propagated along different crystallographic axes. If we write Bardeen's expression a little more generally, we have

$$\frac{\alpha_s}{\alpha_n} = \frac{2}{e^{\varepsilon_0/2kT} + 1}$$

wherein $\varepsilon_0 = \beta k T_c$ is the energy gap at 0°K and $\beta = 3.52$ on the BCS model.

If, however, the gap is anisotropic, β will have different values in different directions. When $\frac{1}{t} \left(\equiv \frac{T_c}{T} \right)$ becomes large, $\log_{10}(\alpha_s/\alpha_n)$ will plot as linear in $1/t$, and the slope will be $-\beta/4.6$; i.e., the zero-point energy gap is determinable. Figure 95 shows such a plot for three

[1] Morse, Olsen, and Gavenda, *Phys. Rev. Letters*, **3**:15 (1959).

different crystallographic directions in the tin monocrystal. The slopes of these lines yield the following values for the constant β:

Crystal direction	β
[100]	4.3 ± 0.2
[110]	3.8 ± 0.1
[001]	3.2 ± 0.1
BCS	3.52

As we have seen, the method does not yield α_s directly—it is necessary to extrapolate the attenuation to 0°K in order to correct for the

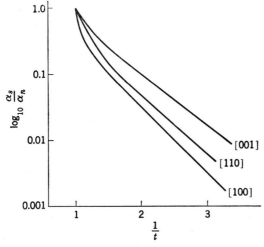

FIG. 95. The log of the attenuation ratio versus the reciprocal of the reduced temperature for three crystallographic directions in a tin single crystal. (*Morse et al.*, 1959.)

lattice term. This necessity, of course, limits the reliability of the technique. Nevertheless, it seems difficult to interpret the results in any manner other than an anisotropy in the energy gap.

SUPERCONDUCTING ALLOYS

Through the years a very considerable experimental effort has been put into the study of superconducting alloys and intermetallic compounds, and it would take us too far afield to discuss much of this work in detail. We may say, however, that such substances almost never show anything approaching a complete Meissner effect. In other words, $B \neq 0$—there is frozen-in flux resulting in a permanent magnetic moment when the field is relaxed. As a matter of fact, the "ideal" case of perfect diamagnetism is only rarely observed, requiring fairly elaborate precautions as to specimen purity and handling (to avoid strains) of the material.

The superconducting compounds, in general, fall into three classes. Thus, for two-component systems, they may be (1) both superconducting components (e.g., PbIn), (2) one component superconducting and the other not (e.g., SnAg), or (3) neither component superconducting (e.g., LiBi). Alloys, in general, exhibit diffuse transitions in a longitudinal magnetic field; on the other hand, many of the intermetallic compounds, such as KBi_2, show fairly sharp transitions. This behavior is exhibited by pure elements also. Thus pure Sn and Hg, which are so-called "soft" superconductors, show sharp transitions, whereas "hard" superconductors like Ta are diffuse.

It is very difficult to produce alloys and intermetallic compounds which are homogeneous, i.e., without composition fluctuations throughout the volume of the specimen. It is thought that such materials have a spongelike structure with superconducting threads embedded in a nonsuperconducting matrix. As such they will clearly exhibit zero resistance but a very incomplete Meissner effect, which is indeed observed.

We recall that the BCS theory cannot predict precisely which substance will become a superconductor apart from the generalization that normally good conductors will not likely be such. As a result of an extensive study of alloys, however, Matthias[1] has proposed an empirical rule (Fig. 96) wherein the transition temperature is plotted against the number of valence electrons per atom. This last quantity can, of course, be varied by employing a series of alloy compositions. These results indicate that metals possessing either five or seven valence electrons per atom have the highest transition temperatures; i.e., they most readily become superconductors.

Very early in this chapter we said that no (1) monovalent element nor (2) ferromagnetic element is observed to be a superconductor. Both these statements are correct and, since monovalent elements are, in general, good electrical conductors, part 1 follows from the BCS model. It has generally been supposed that (2) follows since the internal Weiss field in a ferromagnet would inevitably quench the superconductivity and thus render it unobservable. As a matter of fact, the interesting suggestion has been made by Ginsburg that superconductivity be looked for in very small particles (colloids) of a ferromagnetic whose size is less than the ferromagnetic domain size—an experiment which, to this writer's knowledge, has not so far been attempted. In any event, the ferromagnet with its highly polarized spin states would appear a poor candidate for superconductivity in the light of the BCS model.

In view of all this, it came as a considerable surprise when Matthias,

[1] B. T. Matthias, *Phys. Rev.*, **97**:74 (1955).

Suhl, and Corenzwit[1] succeeded in producing a ferromagnetic super-conductor in the ternary alloy, e.g., $Ce_{0.94}Gd_{0.06}Ru_2$. The way in which this discovery came about is illustrated in Fig. 97, in which both the superconducting transition temperature T_c and the ferromagnetic Curie point[2] T_F are plotted as a function of the per cent of $GdRu_2$ in the alloy. As the curve shows, by lowering the temperature of a sample containing say 8 per cent gadolinium, first the onset of ferro-magnetism is seen at ~5.3°K, followed by a superconducting transition at ~3°K.

The interpretation of this experiment involves considerable difficulty because alloy superconductors, in general, show an incomplete Meissner

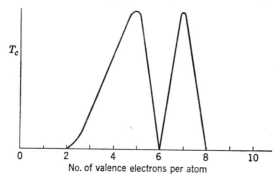

FIG. 96. Relation between the superconducting transition temperature T_c and the number of valence electrons per atom based on alloy studies. (*Matthias*, 1955.)

effect. In other words, it is most difficult to distinguish experimentally between an external magnetic field which is due to ferromagnetic remanence on the one hand and a "frozen-in" magnetic moment on the other. The authors point out, however, that this observed field is more than an order of magnitude larger than the frozen-in flux which is observed in other typical superconductors.

Very much depends on the techniques which the authors employ in their experiments, a point which, owing to the brevity of the report, is not entirely clear. Thus if the specimen is cooled in a steady (weak) magnetic field and the flux observed in a coil surrounding it, we should see an increase in flux on passing T_F followed by a decrease in passing T_c. This, presumably, is what we observe. In addition, of course, the resistance of the specimen must vanish when T_c has been passed.

If we take the result at face value, an interpretive difficulty of a second type develops. This is the question as to how superconduc-

[1] Matthias, Suhl, and Corenzwit, *Phys. Rev. Letters*, **1**:449 (1958).
[2] The temperature at which the spontaneous magnetization vanishes in a ferro-magnetic.

tivity and ferromagnetism can coexist on an atomic scale. As is well known, ferromagnetism occurs only when electron spins are strongly paired because of exchange interaction, and the energies involved are high—much higher than the BCS energy gap. We should therefore expect a ferromagnet to be a normal, rather than superconducting, metal. In other words, combined ferromagnetism and superconductivity on an atomic scale would present a most serious dilemma to the BCS theory. On the other hand, if ferromagnetism and superconductivity merely occur *in the same specimen*, the difficulty is very much less acute. We could, for instance, conceive of the alloy as consisting of a ferromagnet with regions, or threads, of perhaps some-

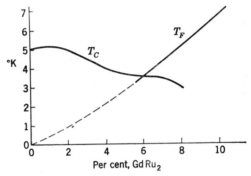

FIG. 97. The superconducting transition temperature T_c and the ferromagnetic Curie temperature T_F for the ternary alloy (Ce, Gd) Ru$_2$ as a function of composition. (*Matthias et al.*, 1958.)

what different composition interlacing it. These, if very thin, could have very large threshold fields.

Matthias and Suhl,[1] in a later communication, have proposed an explanation of their discovery along lines which resemble this. Their suggestion is that the superconducting regions extend only through the thickness of the ferromagnetic domain walls, implying that in such regions the composition of the alloy is not different from that inside the domains.

At the domain walls sharp changes in the spin orientations must occur; the usual mechanism for inducing a permanent moment in a ferromagnet is via the growth of domains, originally pointing in the applied field direction, at the expense of differently oriented neighbors. This means that over a short but finite distance at a wall the spin directions are changing rapidly. Such a region would therefore appear very "unferromagnetic," and the conflict with the BCS model would, therefore, largely disappear.

[1] B. T. Matthias and H. Suhl, *Phys. Rev. Letters,* **4**:51 (1960).

Appendix 1.

THE SUPERCONDUCTING ELEMENTS

Element	T_c, °K	Element	T_c, °K
Tc	11.2	Th	1.37
Nb	8.70	Al	1.20
Pb	7.20	Ga	1.10
La	5.40	Zn	0.90
V	4.89	U	0.80
Ta	4.38	Os	0.71
Hg	4.17	Cd	0.56
Sn	3.73	Zr	0.55
In	3.40	Ru	0.47
Tl	2.39	Ti	0.39
Re	1.70	Hf	0.37*

* This element is uncertain.

SOURCE: B. Serin, *Handbuch der Physik*, vol. 15, p. 230, 1956.

Appendix 2.   Bibliography

I have consulted all the following books, at various times, in the course of preparing this text.   The list is by no means exhaustive.

1. Burton, E., H. Grayson Smith, and J. Wilhelm: "Phenomena at the Temperature of Liquid Helium," Reinhold Publishing Corporation, New York, 1940.

> This book, which is now unfortunately very much out of date, is one of the earliest monographs on liquid helium extant.   It consists of a broad treatment of low-temperature phenomena of all kinds (including some solid-state topics) that were known in 1940.   The treatment is from the physical point of view with a minimum of mathematical analysis.   Parts of the work can still be read with profit today.

2. Keesom, W. H.: "Helium," Elsevier Press, Inc., Houston, Tex., 1942. This edition, which was for a time out of print, has recently (1959) been republished.

> This text, which is almost the bible of low-temperature physicists, is also somewhat out of date but less so than the first book above.   It is an extraordinarily comprehensive treatment of the element helium in all its aspects including spectroscopic data.   The larger part of the book, however, is concerned with liquid helium mainly from the experimental point of view.   It is a valuable source book for finding out about the "classical" experiments on liquid helium (for example, specific-heat measurements) which were carried out mainly at Leiden between 1920 and 1940.   It is a required book in any specialist's library.

3. Andronikashvili, E., and E. Lifshitz: "Supplement to Helium," Moscow, 1949, English translation by Consultant's Bureau, Inc., New York, 1959.

This small volume, as its name suggests, was an attempt to bring Keesom's work up to date after the war. At present the supplement itself is out of date but is a useful addition to the old volume.

4. Shoenberg, D.: "Superconductivity," Cambridge University Press, New York, 1952.

This very good text was first published in 1938 and is at present in its third edition (the above reference is for the second edition). The work treats the whole subject of superconductivity with main emphasis on the experimental side. The mathematical treatment, while generally adequate, is not difficult. In its latest edition it is probably the best book available on this subject in English. The advances on the theoretical side in the past 3 years have, however, been formidable, and these postdate the book. In general, highly recommended.

5. Gorter, C. J. (ed.): "Progress in Low Temperature Physics," Interscience Publishers, Inc., New York, vol. I, 1955; vol. II, 1957.

Volume I consists of 18 chapters, each by a different author who is a specialist in the particular topic he treats. Volume II consists of 14 similar chapters. As is to be expected in this type of review article compendium, the treatment from chapter to chapter is very uneven, albeit the list of authors reads like a Who's Who of contemporary low-temperature physicists and chemists. Some chapters (e.g., Feynman's in vol. I) are as excellent as anything that has appeared in print, but others are of surprisingly poor quality. Nevertheless, the work is useful as a reference.

6. London, F.: "Superfluids," John Wiley & Sons, Inc., New York, vol. I, 1950; vol. II, 1954.

These two short books are a "must" for all low-temperature physicists, students and specialists alike. Volume I deals with superconductivity and vol. II with superfluid helium. The emphasis in both is overwhelmingly theoretical. Volume I contains a very full account of the origins and development of F. and H. London's celebrated phenomenological theory of superconductivity, as well as other material on topics such as the "intermediate state" in superconductors. It predates, of course, the BCS theory. Volume II contains a very complete discussion of the Bose condensation approach to the theory of superfluid helium—an approach which London himself favored. Nevertheless, Landau's viewpoint is not neglected. This volume is noted for many forward-looking ideas (e.g., helium in rotation). Both volumes are unreservedly recommended.

7. Garrett, C. G. B.: "Magnetic Cooling," John Wiley & Sons, Inc., New York, 1954.

This short work is a very good introduction, both experimental and theoretical, to the field of ultra-low temperatures. It contains useful data on many of the salts employed in this kind of work.

8. Simon, F., N. Kurti, J. F. Allen, and K. Mendelssohn: "Low Temperature Physics: Four Lectures," Academic Press, Inc., New York, 1952.

As the title indicates, this monograph consists of four chapters, one by each of the authors. Simple and nonmathematical in approach, it is nevertheless excellent from the point of view of both subject matter and clarity. Among others, the topics treated include superconductivity, liquid helium, and magnetic temperatures. Highly recommended.

9. Atkins, K. R.: "Liquid Helium," Cambridge University Press, New York, 1959.

Of the same format as, and intended as a companion piece to, Schoenberg's "Superconductivity," this book is rather different in its approach. It leans more to the theoretical side than its predecessor. Very wide in coverage, it has a tendency to quote theoretical results with either a lack of, or a minimum of, proof. This tends to make the book somewhat difficult, in some passages, for the student. Nevertheless, it will certainly repay a careful reading.

10. White, G. K.: "Experimental Techniques in Low Temperature Physics," Oxford University Press, New York, 1959.

This useful book is of a quite different nature from any of those quoted above. It concerns itself purely with the technical aspects of experimentation at low temperatures. The book should be most valuable for anyone who wishes to perform experiments in the liquid-helium temperature region.

Index